PRENTICE-HALL FOUNDATIONS OF MODERN *Genetics* SERIES

Sigmund R. Suskind and Philip E. Hartman, Editors

AGRICULTURAL GENETICS *James L. Brewbaker*
GENE ACTION *Philip E. Hartman and Sigmund R. Suskind*
EXTRACHROMOSOMAL INHERITANCE *John L. Jinks*
DEVELOPMENTAL GENETICS * *Clement Market*
HUMAN GENETICS *Victor A. McKusick*
POPULATION GENETICS AND EVOLUTION *Lawrence E. Mettler*
THE MECHANICS OF INHERITANCE *Franklin W. Stahl*
CYTOGENETICS *Carl P. Swanson, Timothy Merz, and William J. Young*

* Published jointly in Prentice-Hall's *Developmental Biology Series*

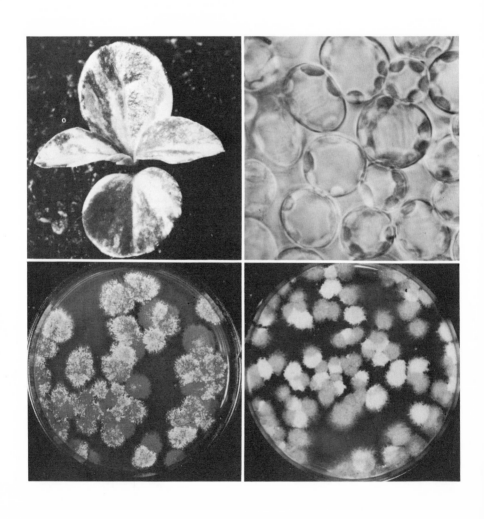

EXTRACHROMOSOMAL INHERITANCE

John L. Jinks

University of Birmingham

PRENTICE-HALL, INC. Englewood Cliffs, New Jersey

FOUNDATIONS OF MODERN GENETICS SERIES

© *Copyright 1964*
by PRENTICE-HALL, INC.
Englewood Cliffs, New Jersey
All rights reserved. No part of this
book may be reproduced in any form,
by mimeograph or any other means,
without permission in writing from
the publishers.
Printed in the United States of America
Library of Congress Catalog Card Number:
64-16032

Extrachromosomal Inheritance
C-29817-P   C-29818-C

PRENTICE-HALL INTERNATIONAL, INC., *London*
PRENTICE-HALL OF AUSTRALIA, PTY., LTD., *Sydney*
PRENTICE-HALL OF CANADA, LTD., *Toronto*
PRENTICE-HALL OF INDIA (PRIVATE) LTD., *New Delhi*
PRENTICE-HALL OF JAPAN, INC., *Tokyo*
PRENTICE-HALL DE MEXICO, S.A., *Mexico City*

Frontispiece. Somatic segregation of extrachromosomal
differences.

Top left. Somatic segregation of normal and mutant
plastids in a seeding of privet.
Photograph courtesy of R.A.E. Tilney-Bassett,
Department of Botany, Oxford.

Top right. Somatic segregation of normal (dark)
and mutant (light) plastids in the palisade
cells of *Epilobium hirsutum.*
Photograph courtesy of Peter Michaelis,
Max-Planck-Institute, Köln-Vogelsang.

Bottom left. Somatic segregation of extrachromosomally
inherited sexuality differences within a
clone of *Aspergillus nidulans.*
Photograph courtesy of my colleagues
J. H. Croft and Morris Grindle.

Bottom right. Somatic segregation of the "red"
extrachromosomal variant of *Aspergillus nidulans.*
Photograph courtesy of my colleagues
J. H. Croft and Morris Grindle.

Foundations of Modern Genetics

Genetic research is alive with excitement and revolutionary advances. Important to the development of science and to the evolution of social structure, genetic thought is widening its impact on many areas: immunology, protein chemistry, cellular physiology, developmental biology, medicine, agriculture, and industry.

So many partnerships and such rapidly expanding methodology demand a fresh approach to genetic training —an approach attempted in this series.

The basic principles of genetics are few and simple. We present them with enough description of accessory scientific areas to allow comprehension not only of the principles themselves but also of the types of experiments from which the concepts have evolved. Such an approach compels the reader to ask: What is the *evidence* for this concept? What are its *limitations?* What are its *applications?*

The Prentice-Hall Foundations of Modern Genetics Series presents the evidence upon which *current* genetic thought is based. It is neither a history nor a survey of all genetic knowledge. The short volumes make possible a stimulating, selective treatment of the various aspects of genetics at the intermediate level, and sectional divisions allow free choice of emphasis in differently oriented college genetics courses.

The references cited in each volume and the current

research literature are the immediate sequels to this series, but the true sequel remains in the hands of the alert reader. He will find here the seed of more than one enigma, the solution of which he, himself, may help bring into man's comprehension sometime in the future.

SIGMUND R. SUSKIND
PHILIP E. HARTMAN

McCollum-Pratt Institute
The Johns Hopkins University

Preface

The once widespread opinion that extrachromosomal inheritance is so rare a phenomenon that it must be regarded as an exception of minor importance is no longer tenable. From the earliest days of genetics the evidence for the existence of extrachromosomal inheritance has been firmly based on a few irrefutable examples in higher plants. Over the years these have been supplemented until today we have examples in representatives of almost every major group of organisms. In choosing illustrative examples I have tried to convey the breadth of the present-day support for extrachromosomal inheritance, but I have emphasized principles rather than examples. The examples set forth here by no means exhaust the list.

After two introductory chapters, the book falls into four main sections. The first, Chapters 3-6, deals with the criteria of extrachromosomal inheritance and presents the evidence that has been collected by their application; the second, Chapters 8 and 9, deals with the nature of the extrachromosomal system and as such is the most controversial section. The third section, Chapters 10 and 11, examines the relationships between the chromosomal and extrachromosomal systems and the fourth, Chapters 12 and 13, concerns the extrachromosomal role in development, variation, and evolution.

A knowledge of Mendelian genetics and the chromosome theory of heredity is assumed. Only brief reminders of relevant features are given. At the appropriate places novel properties of chromosomal genes are discussed in some detail because they often overlap with extrachromosomal phenomena.

Explicitly in the second section, and perhaps implicitly elsewhere, I have laid myself open to the criticism that alternative interpretations of particular instances of extrachromosomal inheritance in terms of "steady state" systems receive inadequate attention. The bias is deliberate. The determinants of extrachromosomal inheritance detected by our criteria share with chromosomal genes the properties of stability, mutability, segregation of alternative forms, maintenance of identity in the "heterozygous" state, and even the possibility of identity at the molecular level. Therefore, I can see no justification for a dichotomy in interpretation between the determinants of chromosomal heredity and those of extrachromosomal heredity.

I am indebted to my colleagues in the Department of Genetics, University of Birmingham, particularly Professor Kenneth Mather, Dr. Morris Grindle, and James H. Croft for innumerable discussions of the subject matter and for critically reading portions of the text.

J.L.J.

Contents

Cell Heredity

The chromosome theory of heredity has rightly become the cornerstone of genetics. The early identification of the chromosomal material of the cell as the bearer of the hereditary determinants, the genes, brought together the two most powerful tools for the experimental investigation of heredity, namely microscopic observations of chromosome behavior and precise breeding procedures for determining inherited characteristics in successive generations.

The immediate and continued success of this dual approach, however, led to the extensive study of chromosome heredity almost to the exclusion of study of the remainder of the cell. And yet, from the beginnings of genetics as a science, there have been constant reminders that the less easily defined extrachromosomal complement should not be ignored. No sooner had chromosomal heredity, with its Mendelian laws of inheritance, been defined and techniques for its recognition developed, than exceptions were described. As far back as 1909, C. Correns and E. Baur found instances of non-Mendelian inheritance for differences in the photosynthetic systems of strains of some flowering plants. Although correctly interpreted as examples of extrachromosomal heredity, these and the many similar examples that were described in the following years remained for a long time a miscellaneous collection of apparently unrelated oddities.

Indeed, these scattered exceptions to Mendelian inheritance aroused little interest in extrachromosomal heredity. But the natural extension of interests from the mechanism of the transmission of chromosomal genes to a consideration of their control of metabolism and development has led to continuing investigation of the extrachromosomal complement of the cell. The cell is now recognized as an integrated unit whose properties are more than a mere composite of its chromosomal and extrachromosomal contents.

Cell phenotype

The cooperation of the chromosomal and extrachromosomal components of the cell in producing the cell phenotype can be illustrated by an important attribute of plant cells, namely, their ability to carry out photosynthesis. This property depends on the presence in the cell of extrachromosomal structures, the plastids, and their associated pigments. The development and activity of the plastids are controlled both by heritable and by environmental factors. Light is the most important of the latter. Development of the plastids usually is not completed in the absence of light. Mutations at a number of chromosomal loci lead to a failure or upset in the development of the plastids and of the pigments they bear. These loci show strict Mendelian inheritance. Abnormal plastids may also occur in cells with a normal chromosomal gene complement, growing in an environment that is ideal for plastid development and activity. This condition is heritable, but the pattern of inheritance is non-Mendelian. At cell division, the cells with the abnormal plastids give rise to other cells that also possess the same kind of abnormal plastids, but only the maternal parent may regularly transmit this condition to the offspring of an outcross. Its determinants are extrachromosomal. Hence this important aspect of the cell phenotype is under the joint control of chromosomal, extrachromosomal, and environmental agencies.

The cell concept

The idea that the cell is an integrated unit and, indeed, the basic unit of life predates genetics itself. In its original form, the "Cell Theory" regarded an organism as a sum of vital units, each of which bore the complete characteristics of its life. The cell was not only equated to the vital unit, but was regarded as the ultimate unit of life. As in all useful generalizations in biology, there are exceptions in this instance—the viruses. The status of viruses is debatable. The only time a virus shows the characteristics of life is when it is exploiting the cellular organization of its host.

There are basic units of life smaller than the cell, for example, the gene or the chromosome. There are larger units, for example, tissues, whose properties may transcend those of its component cells. There are even more complex units, such as organs, individuals, and even collections of individuals. But among these biological units the cell is unique, for it is the smallest unit that is totally capable of reproducing another living unit. Only cells can give rise to other cells.

The parts of the cell (Fig. 1.1) must be duplicated in order to duplicate the whole cell. Cytogenetics has shown us that one part of the cell, the chromosomes and the genes that they bear, is precisely

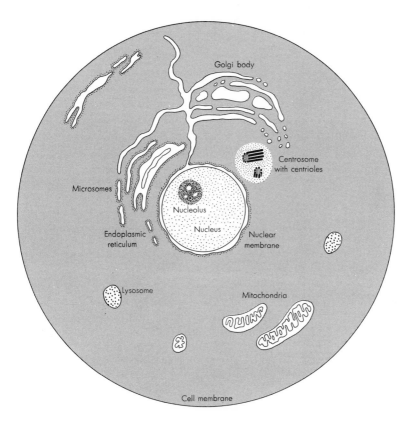

Fig. 1.1. An idealized animal cell, showing some of the more important structures and the relative positions they occupy. An idealized plant cell would be similar, except that an autotrophic cell would contain plastids (see Figs. 2.4 and 2.5) and a flowering plant cell would contain no centrosome. The properties of the various structures are described in the text. After Jean Brachet, "The Living Cell," *Scientific American*, 205 (1961). Reprinted with permission. Copyright © 1961 by Scientific American, Inc. All rights reserved.

duplicated. The chromosomes transmit many properties of the cell from one cell generation to the next. But what of the extrachromosomal complement of the cell? Does it divide at cell division? If so, how precisely and by what mechanism?

Certainly the division of the extrachromosomal complement is often visibly unequal at cell division, but this does not mean that it is qualitatively unequal. Furthermore, there are limits to any inequality that may occur. Some extrachromosomal material is always necessary for continued survival, for chromosomes devoid of this material cannot produce it, nor can they divide. In fact, they show fewer indications of life than the extrachromosomal material alone. This material can at least produce more of itself, and even attempt to divide (although, of course, removal of the chromosome complement, while it may not cause immediate death, severely limits the powers of reproduction and differentiation of a cell). It would appear, therefore, that the duplication of extrachromosomal material is necessary to generate an entire cell, and that extrachromosomal material must be present for cell duplication to occur.

Two methods, microscopy and experimental breeding, led to the elucidation of the behavior of the chromosomes at cell division, and their role in Mendelian inheritance. These methods have also been used in attempts to elucidate the mechanism of duplication of extrachromosomal constituents at cell division, and their relationship to extrachromosomal heredity. In a few instances, cytological investigations have indicated the likely bearers of the extrachromosomally inherited differences, and their behavior at cell division and gametogenesis, but many examples of extrachromosomal heredity are known only through their breeding behavior. Their classification as extrachromosomal depends almost exclusively on peculiarities in their transmission in controlled breeding experiments. Since the majority of examples fall into this category, they constitute an important part of the existing evidence for extrachromosomal heredity. The criteria on which these examples are accepted as extrachromosomal, therefore, assume enormous importance. Hence the nature and validity of these criteria must be the primary concern of any study of extrachromosomal heredity. Pertinent questions—on the nature of the hereditary system responsible for extrachromosomal heredity, on the structural and functional relationships between this system and the chromosomal system, and on the role of the extrachromosomal system in heredity, development, and evolutionary change—can be meaningfully answered only after valid rules for the recognition of extrachromosomal heredity have been established.

Terminology

If we are to subdivide the hereditary material of the cell into chromosomal and extrachromosomal components we must have a system of nomenclature that conveys the differences and homologies between the two systems. Unfortunately, no simple, comprehensive nomenclature comparable with that currently in use in chromosomal heredity has yet evolved for extrachromosomal heredity; some consistent terminology is badly needed.

The terminology of this book will be based on recent proposals by Peter Michaelis and Donald F. Jones; an outline, derived from their proposals, of the principal subdivisions of the hereditary material of the cell is given in Fig. **1.2.** The term *plasmon*, introduced by Fritz von Wettstein in 1924, will refer to the largest unit, the total extrachromosomal hereditary complement of a cell. It will thus be the equivalent of *genome* (the total chromosomal complement). By analogy with *homozygote* and *heterozygote*, *homoplasmon* and *heteroplasmon* will describe cells in which all the representatives or homologues of a particular extrachromosomal hereditary determinant are alike or not alike, respectively. The smallest heritable unit in the plasmon will be identified by *plasmagene*, a term introduced by Cyril D. Darlington in 1939. The relationship between a plasmagene and the plasmon is thus homologous to that of a gene and the genome. Plasmagenes have been subdivided by various authors, mainly on the basis of their alleged carriers. For example, the term *plastogene*, introduced by Y.

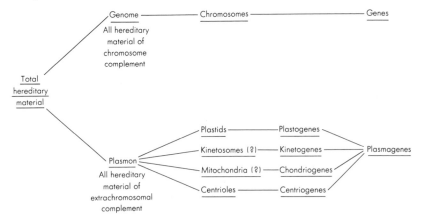

Fig. 1.2. The principal subdivisions of the total hereditary material of the cell, showing the homology of extrachromosomal terminology with chromosomal terminology.

Imai in 1937 and widely used since, describes those plasmagenes that are transmitted as though borne on a plastid and that determine the likeness of daughter to parent plastid. Those plasmagenes that appear to be attached to other extrachromosomal structures, such as kinetosomes and mitochondria will be referred to by similar terms, namely, *kinetogenes* and *chondriogenes* respectively.

References

Darlington, Cyril D., *The Evolution of Genetic Systems*. New York: The Macmillan Company, 1939.

Jones, Donald F., "The Genotype as the Sum of Plasmatype and Chromotype," *Am. Naturalist, 94* (1960), 181.

Michaelis, Peter, "Cytoplasmic Inheritance in *Epilobium* and Its Theoretical Significance," *Advan. Genet., 6* (1954), 287.

Extrachromosomal Cell Constituents
with Physical Continuity

There are two classes of extrachromosomal cell constituents that have important functions and conceivably may have physical continuity. These are the fiber-producers, which control movement within cells as well as movement of whole cells, and the controllers of cell metabolism. It is among these that the bearers of extrachromosomal hereditary determinants will be sought. Extrachromosomal bodies must satisfy a number of criteria before their role as bearers of hereditary determinants can be accepted. They must determine some characteristic of the cell. They must duplicate and be self-duplicating in the sense that, if lost, they cannot be regenerated by chromosomal material. They must be distributed to daughter cells during cell division.

The properties of the recognizable extrachromosomal cell constituents, most of which are shown in Fig. 1.1, will now be examined in the light of these criteria.

The fiber-producers

The fiber-producers are variously identified: (1) as centrosomes, with or without a central granule (a centriole), which generate asters during cell division, and (2) as basal granules or blepharoplasts, which generate cilia, flagella, and sperm tails. Centrosomes are universally present in animals and lower plants, and blepharoplasts are present wherever a free-swimming motile stage is found. Thus there are two categories of cellular activity: initiation of the spherical asters, which may or may not lead to the appearance of optically distinct fibers, and the generation of fibrils along a single axis.

Centrioles

In many animals the centrioles can be seen to divide and duplicate, and to show visible continuity from one cell generation to another. Many observers have traced the centriole through the life history of various cells, both by light and by electron microscopy. Furthermore, this continuity extends to the gametes, and thereby from one sexual generation to another. In fact, minute particles, representing parts of the centriole, are the only residual protein found in the sperm heads of some animals.

The centrioles are generally found in pairs, lying at right angles to one another (Fig. 2.1). Each cell possesses a pair, and each pair gives

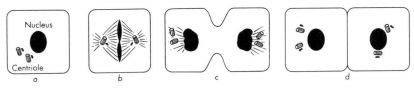

Fig. 2.1. The reproductive cycle of centrioles, according to Daniel Mazia. (a) Before nuclear division begins, there are two fully formed centrioles lying together outside the nuclear membrane. Each has the beginnings of a new centriole forming at right angles to it. (b) By metaphase the old centrioles, accompanied by the partly formed new ones, have moved apart to occupy the poles of the spindle. (c) At telophase each daughter cell has two fully formed centrioles at right angles to each other. Of each pair of centrioles, one is old and one is new. (d) The centriolar cycle is starting again in each of the daughter cells. This interpretation assumes that the complex cylindrical structure of the centriole is reproduced generatively and not by fission. After Daniel Mazia, "How Cells Divide," *Scientific American*, 205 (1961). Reprinted with permission. Copyright © 1961 by Scientific American, Inc. All rights reserved.

rise to another as the cell divides. Two methods of replication have been suggested for centrioles: fission and generative reproduction. Reproduction by fission implies that each part of the parent unit duplicates itself and gives half of its substance to each daughter. In generative reproduction, only part of the parent unit reproduces itself and this provides the framework for the development of a new unit. The most recent observations, particularly those of L. R. Cleveland on the flagellate *Barbulanympha* (Fig. 2.2), suggest that the centriole does not divide at all. Rather, the parent centriole generates a small "infant," which grows to maturity while still attached to the parent by a thin strand. On the basis of this type of observation, Daniel Mazia has proposed that the complex, three-dimensional centriole produces a master molecule, carrying all the information for making a new centriole. He interprets the sequence of events at cell division as depicted diagrammatically in Fig. 2.1. The new centriole first appears as an outgrowth from the parent, developing at right angles to the old.

Once they have reproduced, the centrioles move apart to produce their characteristic activity during cell division.

The structure of the centrioles as seen by light microscopy is highly variable, and in extreme cases they are not visible at all, or are seen only at certain stages of cell division. Electron microscopy, on the other hand, has provided a more consistent morphological conception of a centriole. A centriole is a body composed of nine tubules arranged

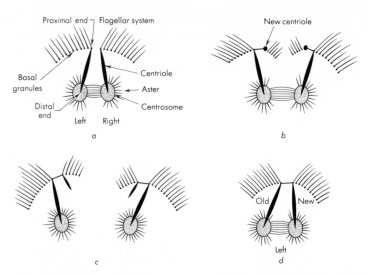

Fig. 2.2. The centriolar reproductive cycle in the flagellate *Barbulanympha*, based on the original drawings of L. R. Cleveland. (a) The two centrioles are elongated; the distal end, which organizes the aster, is enveloped in a centrosome. The proximal end produces the basal granules, which in turn organize the flagellar system. (b and c) Successive stages during cell division. As cell division commences, each centriole begins to reproduce itself at its proximal end, and throughout the process the new centriole produces a new set of basal granules and their associated organelles from its proximal end. (d) One daughter cell at the end of division, when one centriole and half of the flagellar system is old and the other centriole and half of the flagellar system is new. As the cell goes into the next division, the new centriole produces an aster at its distal end. Note that the reproduction of the centriole is generative. The chromosomal material is omitted for clarity. After L. R. Cleveland, "Types and Life Cycles of Centrioles of Flagellates," *J. Protozool., 4* (1957).

cylindrically. This structure bears a remarkable resemblance to that of basal granules and the axial filaments associated with them.

Uncertainties exist regarding the exact function of centrioles. Some workers credit the centriole not only with the production of the asters, but also of the spindle upon which the chromosomes congregate during cell division. Others deny that the centriole even produces the aster. The arguments on centriolar function are less important to the inquiry into their role in extrachromosomal heredity than are denials of their physical continuity. These two aspects, however, are often inseparable in experimental studies, insofar as the presence or absence of a centriole is frequently inferred from the presence or absence of what is accepted as its activities.

The factual basis for questioning that centrioles are self-perpetuating bodies largely rests on the discovery of cytasters, aster-like structures, in "activated" sea urchin and amphibian eggs. An activated egg is one that, after mechanical stimulation, develops parthenogenetically, that is, without fertilization. It therefore lacks the centriole, normally contributed by the sperm and which, according to many observers, produces all the centrioles of the developing embryo. The cytasters may arise in an activated egg after the removal either of the egg nucleus or of the whole mitotic apparatus, including the normal asters. Thus the egg cytoplasm is apparently capable of producing a structure that in appearance and sometimes in function is like an aster.

The latest electron microscopic observations of cytasters of activated sea urchin eggs show a typical centriole, identical in structure to those normally found in fertilized eggs. Furthermore, activated parthenogenetic eggs, which possess only cytasters, subsequently produce cells with cilia and flagella. Evidence presented later suggests that the latter only develop from centrioles, or homologous structures. It does not automatically follow from these observations, however, that centrioles must have an extracentriolar origin.

When present, the sperm centriole is the only one that is active in the zygote. Prior to fertilization centrioles are present in the egg and are active during the cell divisions culminating in its production. It would seem reasonable, therefore, to suppose that a centriole is present in the unfertilized egg but is normally nonfunctional. Indeed, it may even be inhibited by the sperm centriole after fertilization. But in the absence of the latter, there seems to be no reason why the egg centriole could not take over the activities normally carried out by the sperm centriole. A final verdict, however, must await the outcome of electron microscopic searches of the egg cells for further signs of an egg centriole.

Basal granules

From the evidence now available, it seems probable that all cilia, flagella, and axial filaments are derived from particles variously called blepharoplasts, kinetosomes, or basal granules. As the result of an intensive study of the light-microscope cytology of protozoa, André Lwoff claims that cilia and flagella arise from discrete self-duplicating granules. Most protozoologists agree with this interpretation.

As already mentioned, there is a similarity between the structure of the basal granule and the axial filaments they produce and the structure of the centriole. This similarity has been reinforced by observations on the changing role of the centriole during spermatogenesis. The centriole, which normally appears to be the initiator of asters, becomes a producer of sperm tails. Furthermore, electron microscopic comparisons show that the physical relationship between the centriole of a sperm and its tail is the same as that of a basal granule and its cilium or flagellum.

The detailed structure of a sperm tail was first observed in electron micrographs of fowl sperm. These show that a total of eleven fibrils arise from the distal centriole. Two of these fibrils are thicker than the rest, and are surrounded by an outer ring of nine. This general appearance is also found in sperm tails of many different animals, in animal cilia, and in cilia in green and brown algae, bryophytes, and pteridophytes. Similarly, electron micrographs show that the basal granules associated with cilia and flagella have a hollow, cylindrical structure composed of a ring of nine fibrils, previously seen in centrioles. Thus the basic pattern of an outer ring of nine tubules or fibrils occurs in centrioles, basal granules, sperm tails, cilia, and flagella.

The most convincing evidence that the centriole–basal granule complex is self-perpetuating and controls heritable properties of the cell comes from investigations into the ciliates. In these organisms, the arrangement of the basal granules (kinetosomes) in characteristic rows (kineties) is responsible for most of the visible differentiation. The kinetosomes are pluripotent; a single one may, by division, yield daughter granules that participate in different functions. Some granules appear to generate cilia, while others produce a variety of fibrillar structures, for example, trichocysts, which play an important role in morphogenesis.

The consequences of losing or gaining kinetosomes vary from one ciliate to another. *Stentor* can regenerate a complete animal from a nucleated fragment equivalent to one sixty-fourth of the body. Vance Tartar has shown, however, that nucleated fragments entirely devoid of cortical material (in which the kinetosomes are contained) can neither regenerate nor produce the feeding organelles. Thus the cortex or some component of it, such as the kinetosomes, is apparently essential for regeneration, and hence presumably possesses physical continuity. Since any region of the cortex can give rise to all others during regeneration, all regions of the cortex and the kinetosomes they contain must be equipotent. There is no regional differentiation.

In *Licnophora macfarlandi* the cortical ciliary system shows a primitive differentiation into an oral and a basal region. If the oral region is removed, it is regenerated from the basal region; the basal region cannot be regenerated. It appears that basal kinetosomes can only arise from other basal kinetosomes.

Many visible structures of the cortical system of *Paramecium aurelia* appear to be determined by their own persisting organization. Almost every loss or gain of cortical material is perpetuated during cell division. Tracy M. Sonneborn observed the reproduction of animals with double, incompletely double, single, and incomplete sets of cortical structures, and he recently has been able to establish the origin and development of these structures. The mouth and gullet, and their kineties, arise only beside and under the influence of a pre-existing mouth and gullet. Similarly, the diverse pattern of kineties to the right and left of the oral meridian arises from the differential growth of pre-existing kineties. Other structures that are not produced by direct replication of a pre-existing model nevertheless are still ultimately under the control of the kinety pattern. For example, the cell anus (cytopygae) arises whenever the posterior right and left kinety patterns are juxtaposed. Thus in *Paramecium*, kinetosomes arise not only from pre-existing kinetosomes, but particular kinetosomes appear to arise only from their pre-existing counterparts, which occupy the same position in the cortical pattern. Whether this differentiation is inherent in the kinetosomes or a secondary effect of the position they occupy in the pattern is not clear from these observations. In either interpretation, the kinetosomes play an important role as initiators or translators of cortical differentiation patterns. These patterns, in turn, are perpetuated from one cell generation to another.

The sequence of events during regeneration of transected *Licnophora* partially clarifies the role of the kinetosomes. The kinety fibrillar system starts regenerating first, growing beyond the edge of the non-fibrillar cortical material and extending freely into the surrounding culture medium. Only later does the nonfibrillar cortical material enclose the fibers. Thus the kinetosomes and their associated fibrillar system, rather than the cortical groundwork, appear to be primary determiners of the cortical pattern and shape.

Although in the ciliates the centriole and kinetosome are structurally homologous, there is no indication that one can give rise to the other. The two behave as independent, self-maintaining systems. In the flagellates, however, the flagellar system is directly or indirectly controlled by the centriolar system. In *Barbulanympha*, the two centrioles are elongated, and their distal ends, which organize the asters, are enveloped in centrosomes. During cell division, each centriole reproduces itself once at its proximal end, and each new centriole begins to produce numerous small basal granules. The granules, in turn, generate a new flagellar system with its associated organelles, the parabasal bodies and axostyles, throughout the process of cell division. Thus following division, half the flagellar system of the daughter cell is old and half is new. In this cycle, each centriole produces a new centriole and the flagellar system from its proximal end in the first cell generation, the aster from its distal end in the second, and so on. Fig. **2.2**, based on L. R. Cleveland's original drawings, illustrates this cycle.

Although it is possible that the centriole produces only one or a few basal granules, and that these give rise to the others, there can be no doubt that in *Barbulanympha* the centriole initiates the process. During the course of his investigations, Cleveland observed numerous aberrant individuals that were produced by multiple fusion of gametes, or by the fusion of defective gametes. Some had an excess, others a shortage, of centrioles; in some, the centrioles were wrongly sited, in others, they did not exist at all. In all individuals, asters and flagella were produced by the centrioles, irrespective of their numbers and the positions they occupied in the cell. Where centrioles were absent, neither asters nor flagella were produced.

Is there some inherent property of centrioles and the basal granules derived from them that determines their different activities? Or can their activities be attributed to some property of the local cytoplasm in which the centrioles happen to lie? The evidence is inconclusive, but there is good reason to believe that the fiber-producers satisfy the minimal requirements for considering an extrachromosomal cell component as a bearer of hereditary information.

Metabolic controllers

Mitochondria

The mitochondria and the plastids are the principal metabolic controllers providing evidence of physical continuity from one cell generation to the next. The mitochondria are essential constituents of the animal cells on which most experimental investigations have been carried out; they are presumed to have equal significance in plant cells. While the universal occurrence of mitochondria is not in itself proof of their physical continuity, it is indicative of an important role in cell metabolism.

The physical continuity of mitochondria through male gametes has been demonstrated cytologically in several species of centrurid scorpions. The mitochondria divide transversely during spermatogenesis, and each spermatid receives two mitochondria. The scorpion *Opisthacanthus*, on the other hand, has twenty-four mitochondria in its primary spermatocytes. These are usually divided equally, so that the four spermatids receive six mitochondria. The division is only approximate, however; in a sample of five hundred spermatids, 76 per cent had six, 17 per cent five, and 7 per cent had seven mitochondria.

The most detailed account of the behavior of mitochondria during gamete production has been given by R. Barer and S. Joseph in their photographic and cinematographic studies of spermatogenesis in living cells of grasshoppers. As the first of the two meiotic divisions begins, the mitochondria are arranged in crescentic clumps close to the nuclear membrane. By metaphase they have accumulated at the equator of the spindle, where they become more compact and appear to surround the chromosomes. At the approach of anaphase, they are arranged in two fairly dense sheaves. Thereafter, a cleavage furrow appears in the cell wall and pushes the sheaves toward the center of the cell. As this furrow deepens, the mitochondrial material thins in the center and appears to accumulate in the daughter cells. Completion of the cleavage furrow produces two fully formed secondary spermatocytes.

At the second meiotic division this process is repeated, except that two very dark clumps of mitochondrial material can be seen where the sheaves enter the daughter cells. These become the so-called Nebenkern, which consist of tightly packed, spherical granules. In locusts, the Nebenkern has been seen to pass down to the sperm tail to form the so-called mitochondrial sheath.

The division of mitochondria during mitotic cell division has been followed in detail in tissue cultures of fibroblast cells by phase microscopy and cinematography. The mitochondria in the vicinity of the nucleus become thinner, fragment, and disappear. The remaining mitochondria are arranged outside the spindle, and are passively and approximately equally divided between the daughter cells. There is no synchronous division of individual mitochondria accompanying nuclear division, but transverse fission is commonly observed at other times, and it must be assumed that replication occurs between each cell division, since each daughter cell receives roughly half the mitochondria present in the mother cell.

Detailed, reliable accounts of the behavior of mitochondria at gamete production and at cell division are rare. Hence it is not known how far the sequence of events just described applies to other types of cells or to other organisms.

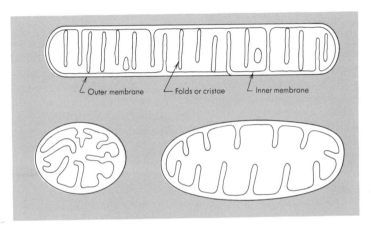

Fig. 2.3. The structure and shapes of mitochondria, as revealed by electron micrographs of sections. These show the characteristic double membrane; the inner membrane is thrown into folds or cristae to produce a large internal surface.

The shape of mitochondria may be spherical, rodlike, or filamental. Their shapes differ characteristically from one type of cell to another in the same individual (Fig. 2.3), and they may differ in shape within a single cell. The internal structure of the mitochondrion, as revealed by electron microscopic studies of cell sections, consists of two parts, an enclosing membrane and an inner membrane that is thrown into folds or cristae to produce a large internal surface. The chemical composition of the mitochondria varies, but the principal constituents are protein and lipoid, most of which is phospholipoid.

The mitochondrion is an organized functional unit containing numerous enzymes. Some of these appear to be dissolved in the internal fluid, and escape if the mitochondrion is broken. Others, particularly enzymes capable of oxidizing various acids, are attached in organized arrays to the internal membrane. The multi-enzyme arrays are still organized on small submitochondrial pieces after the mitochondrion has been fragmented. Intact, the mitochondrion breaks down fats and carbohydrates into more oxidizable molecules, and in the process transfers their chemical energy to other molecules, particularly to the high-energy phosphate bonds, such as are found in adenosine triphosphate (ATP).

Many important reactions take place in the mitochondrion, for example, the tricarboxylic acid cycle, in which a succession of organic acids is oxidized to carbon dioxide. See W. D. McElroy's *Cell Physiology and Biochemistry*, 2nd ed. (Prentice-Hall, 1964) for details. The mitochondrion is, in fact, the powerhouse of the cell. The energy it releases and stores in molecules such as ATP is used throughout the cell, wherever it is required for endothermic reactions or for muscle action. It is not surprising, therefore, that mitochondria are very common in active cells, and closely associated with the parts concerned with the activity. For example, they surround the fibrils of muscles, the membranes of water and foot transporters, and the membranes of contractile vacuoles.

There can be no doubt about the essential role of mitochondria in cell metabolism, nor of their contribution to the different metabolic patterns characterizing different tissues. There is ample evidence of their replication and distribution to daughter cells at cell division. There is, however, no evidence that the presence of mitochondria is essential for the production of other mitochondria, although, as we shall see, this property may be inferred from the evidence suggesting that they possess genetic continuity.

Plastids

Plastids are present in all green plants. They may be associated with the photosynthetic properties of the cell (chloroplasts), with the coloring of petals and roots (chromoplasts), or with the storage of starch, oil, or protein (leucoplasts). Because of the importance of chloroplasts, they have been the subject of most of the investigations on physical continuity.

The chloroplast of higher plants (Fig. 2.4) is surrounded by a double membrane that encloses a granular ground substance, generally called the stroma. Embedded in this is a lamellar system, consisting of highly ordered grana lamellae and paired stroma lamellae. In a fully developed chloroplast, the number of stroma and grana lamellae are equal. Wherever lamellae end they are connected in pairs, and thus two adjacent lamellae form discs. In young chloroplasts, stacks of grana lamellae are distributed almost at random, but as the chloroplast matures the grana lamellae form large piles, traversing the whole chloroplast. The detailed structure varies slightly in different plants, but the double envelope with the stacks of closed discs, which is so reminiscent of the mitochondrion, is a constant feature of all chloroplasts.

The multiplication and distribution of chloroplasts at cell division is most easily studied in the lower plants, in which a small and constant number of rather large chloroplasts are present in each cell. By follow-

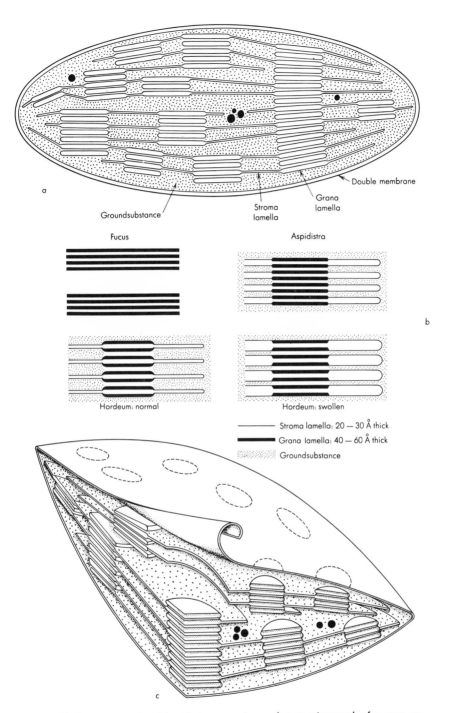

Fig. 2.4. (a) The structure of a chloroplast, as seen in an electron micrograph of a cross section. (b) The variation in the lamellar structure found in different species. Based on the original drawings of Ditter von Wettstein in "Genetics and the Sub-microscopic Cytology of Plastids," *Hereditas*, **43** (1957). (c) The three-dimensional structure of a chloroplast; schematic diagram courtesy of Dr. Ditter von Wettstein.

ing the behavior of the chloroplasts in vegetative cells, gametes, and zygotes of a large number of lower plants—for example, the algae *Zygnema, Spirogyra,* and *Rhychonema* and the liverwort *Anthoceros*—the general conclusion has been reached that they never arise *de novo.* (See the discussion of "Uniparental Transmission" in Chapter 8.)

In the ferns *Selaginella* and *Isoetes,* the meristematic cells contain only one plastid, which divides prior to nuclear division. In the mature cells of *Isoetes,* however, there are many chloroplasts that must all arise by division of this one.

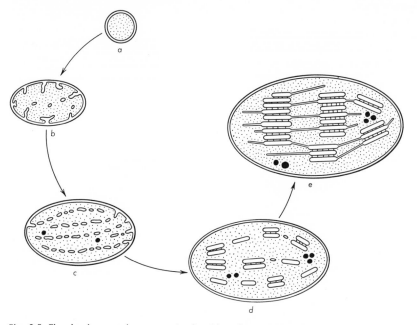

Fig. 2.5. The developmental sequence in the chloroplasts of flowering plants. (a) The proto-plastid consists of a double membrane enclosing a dense stroma. (b) The inner membrane appears to blebb off the vesicles that are present. (c) The vesicles increase in number. (d) Vesicles fuse to form layers of discs, and these multiply and fuse to produce a continuous lamellar system. (e) The stroma and grana portions of the lamellar system become differated. For the final stage, see Fig. 2.4a. After Ditter von Wettstein, "Genetics and the Sub-microscopic Cytology of Plastids," *Hereditas, 43* (1957).

In the embryo and meristematic cells of flowering plants, no chloro-plasts can be seen. There are, however, protoplastids that are not readily distinguishable from mitochondria with the light microscope and that can be seen to divide by fission. The development of the complex chloroplast from the small protoplastid has been studied in many species, including *Aspidistra* barley, corn, tomato, and spruce.

The sequence of events leading to the development of a chloroplast is similar in all these plants; the various stages that have been described by Ditter von Wettstein are shown in Fig. 2.5. It appears that in flowering plants the chloroplasts per se do not have to be transmitted from one cell generation to another to achieve physical continuity. The essential information for their perpetuation can be contained in the simple protoplastid.

This illustrates once more an important point already raised in connection with the reproduction of centrioles; physical continuity does not require that an extrachromosomal entity multiply by fission. What it does require is that a master molecule produced by the entity provide the essential framework for the generation of a new one. Thus the master molecule is the only part of the entity that must possess direct continuity from one cell generation to another. A more important corollary, however, is that an extrachromosomal entity may disappear and reappear at a microscopically visible level at different times in the life cycle, or in different cells of a single individual, without necessarily implying that it is generated *de novo*. This possibility, of course, increases the difficulty of demonstrating the physical continuity of an extrachromosomal structure. The only adequate criterion appears to be the structure's inability to be formed anew once it is removed or lost. This criterion cannot be applied when the structure is vital for cell metabolism, as are the mitochondria and the plastids. Nevertheless, considerable evidence in favor of the physical continuity of chloroplasts has accumulated from studies on species of *Euglena*, which are not obligate autotrophs and can therefore survive the loss of their chloroplasts.

Many treatments—including chemical agents such as streptomycin, antihistamines, and o-methylthreonine, heat (for example, four to six days at 36°C.), and ultraviolet irradiation—render *Euglena gracilis* permanently free of chlorophyll. Growth in the dark produces the same effect in *E. mesnili*. The ability to form chlorophyll is never regained after a return to normal culture conditions. The loss of chlorophyll usually coincides with the loss of recognizable chloroplast structure. Hence it is concluded that new chloroplasts can only arise in cells that already contain at least one chloroplast.

There is evidence, however, that chlorophyll-free cells may be produced and even all sign of chloroplast structure lost with a subsequent complete recovery of both. This happens when *E. gracilis* is cultured in the dark and returned to the light. This evidence is at variance with that of similar experiments with *E. mesnili*, but it does suggest that something in addition to the visible chloroplasts must be lost before the loss becomes irreversible. Such an interpretation is compatible with the origin of chloroplasts from protoplastid precursors.

A convincing cytological demonstration of the physical continuity of chloroplasts in an alga was provided by von Wisselingh in the 1920's. He found a cell of *Spirogyra triformis* containing abnormal as well as normal plastids. Both divided at cell division, producing a lineage, each cell of which contained normal and abnormal plastids. In flowering plants, extensive lineages in which every cell contains both normal and abnormal chloroplasts have been repeatedly observed in a number of species. In the alga and in the higher plants the physical continuity of both normal and abnormal plastids is the most likely explanation of their persistent occurrence in all the cells of a lineage. The significance of the perpetuation of normal and abnormal forms in flowering plants, however, is much greater because it coincides with a type of hereditary transmission that is unmistakably extrachromosomal. (See Chapters 3 and 4.)

The relationship between the various forms of plastid, namely the chloroplasts, chromoplasts, and leucoplasts, whose presence is characteristic of different types of tissue, raises the same problem as that posed by centrioles and kinetosomes. Either the different forms of the plastids are inherent in the plastids themselves or they represent different responses of inherently identical plastids to the different cytoplasmic environments in which they develop. In general, the small colorless plastids found in the roots of most plant species remain unchanged by growing them in the light. Hence growth in the light does not change the colorless root plastids into the green forms normally found in parts of the plant exposed to the light. Thus the difference between these forms of plastid is not purely environmental in origin.

The frequencies with which the same form occurs vary characteristically from one tissue to another. Chloroplasts are, of course, most frequent in the photosynthetic tissue of the leaf. In the epidermis of undersides of leaves, they are usually confined to the stomatal cells. There can be no doubt, therefore, that plastids, like mitochondria, play an essential role as a cause and a result of differentiation.

Other extrachromosomal structures

So far, only those extrachromosomal structures whose function is well established and for which there is cytological evidence for physical continuity from one generation to another have been considered. These structures by no means exhaust the known extrachromosomal constituents of the cell that could conceivably have similar important functions and physical continuity. Other, lesser-known cell constituents are at the present time insufficiently understood to be ranked in importance with mitochondria and plastids. These constituents will be referred to from time to time, however, and some knowledge of their main properties will be helpful.

Kinetoplasts

The kinetoplast is a nucleoprotein body of unknown function and homology found in trypanosomes and certain other protozoa. When these organisms are grown in the presence of acridine dyes, division of the kinetoplast is differentially blocked. After repeated fission under these conditions, a race is produced that is devoid of kinetoplasts. The loss is irreversible, hence the kinetoplast is endowed with physical continuity. On the other hand, its function can be dispensed with without any apparent harm to the organism, thus the kinetoplast is no more essential for immediate survival than are the chloroplasts of *Euglena*. Recent electron microscopic studies suggest that the fine structure of the kinetoplast is similar to that of a mitochondrion, within which are anteroposteriorly orientated anastomosing fibers. The mitochondrial nature of the kinetoplast is also supported by its reaction to stains, such as Janus green B, that are usually specific for mitochondria, but it is discounted by their different chemical compositions.

Endoplasmic reticulum and microsomes

After removing large bodies such as nuclei and mitochondria from cell homogenates, ultracentrifugation invariably separates small structures (microsomes) that are rich in ribonucleic acid (RNA), phospholipoid, and protein. Tissue preparations fixed in osmium tetroxide reveal no microsomes, but they do reveal delicate membranous structures, lined with small RNA-rich granules, in the cytoplasm, which K. R. Porter has called the endoplasmic reticulum. This is present in all cells examined so far, except the adult red blood cells of mammals, and it is particularly well developed in gland cells. The reticulum constitutes an enormous increase in the cell's inner surface. The membranous component of the microsome fraction derived from tissue homogenates is rich in phospholipoid, associated with a protein component. This component may be removed by washing in detergents, leaving free ribonucleoprotein particles (ribosomes). Many now accept the view put forward by G. E. Palade and his collaborators that the microsomes originate as a result of the fragmentation of the delicate endoplasmic reticulum during the homogenization of cells. Many ribosomes are attached to the membranous component, although some are found free in cells of higher organisms. In bacteria, the ribosomes are found throughout the cytoplasm, unassociated with any membranous component.

Electron microscopic studies have suggested that the membranous reticulum arises from the nuclear membrane by a delamination process (see Fig. 1.1). This would fit with the observation that no reticulum is present in anucleate blood cells. Although the origin of ribosomes is essentially unknown, there is general agreement on their main function. They are the sites at which amino acids are incorporated into proteins. (See Philip E. Hartman and Sigmund R. Suskind's *Gene Action*, in this series.) Furthermore, there is a close correlation between the RNA content of a microsomal fraction and the rate of protein synthesis. Hence the suggestion first made by Jean Brachet, that microsomes are concerned in protein synthesis, appears to be proved.

Since the origin of ribosomes is unknown, it would be premature to discuss whether microsomes possess physical continuity. There is, however, evidence that they possess the different, although obviously related, property of self-perpetuation, the ability of an entity to give rise to similar entities under suitable conditions. Although it is clearly an important aspect of physical continuity, there has been no critical demonstration that if the entity possessing the property of self-perpetuation is lost or removed no other cell constituent can produce it. The evidence for self-perpetuation of ribosomes has been obtained by injecting ribosomes on the chorionallantoic membrane of a chick embryo. This causes a local increase in bodies whose staining properties are basophilic, like those of the original ribosomes, and an increase in the activity of an enzyme, glucose-6-phosphate, normally associated with microsomes. Taken together, the increase in basophilic granules and in enzyme activity suggests that the presence of microsomes might lead to the generation of new ones.

Golgi complex

Many controversies have raged concerning the existence and nature of a reticular apparatus, first described by C. Golgi and subsequently named after him. Its role, and even its existence, is still discussed. The electron microscope has, however, revealed a structure that is consistently present in a wide range of tissues, particularly in those with secretory functions. The structure consists of groups of large, empty vacuoles surrounded by concentrically arranged double membranes. Intimately associated with the membranes are small granules that are somewhat larger than those associated with the endoplasmic reticulum. The ability of the Golgi complex to reduce osmium tetroxide suggests the presence of lipides. Although its role is obscure, its more highly developed appearance in secretory cells suggests a secretory function.

Nothing is known with any degree of certainty about the origin, perpetuation, or physical continuity of the Golgi complex.

Lysosomes

Lysosomes is the term originated by C. deDuve for particles that, in centrifugation studies, appeared to be the cell sites of specific hydrolytic enzymes, including acid phosphatase, ribonuclease, deoxyribonuclease, cathepsin, glucuronidase, uricase, and possibly catalase and D-amino oxidase. Electron microscopic studies of liver fractions, which are rich in these enzymes, have revealed particles that are distinct from both mitochondria and microsomes in appearance. These particles are dense and take on a variety of shapes and sizes, and their distribution in the cells coincides with that of acid phosphatase. There is, therefore, a correspondence between the particles recognized in the centrifugation studies and those seen in the electron micrographs. Although the lysosomes clearly are important in the digestive activities of the cell, it is too early to assess their significance, relationships, and origin.

Cell membranes

In unicellular organisms, particularly the ciliates, we have seen that structures associated with the cell cortex possess physical continuity. Multicellular organisms are compartmentalized by membranes presumably similar in structure to the outer boundaries of unicellular organisms, and hence prospectively possessing similar hereditary properties.

Current opinion is that the cell membrane is a structure containing both lipoid and protein components. It is frequently specialized in many ways by evaginations and infoldings, similar to the foldings of the inner membrane of mitochondria, that increase the cellular surface. Clearly, the cell membrane is important in controlling the transport of materials into and out of the cell, and therefore in controlling the metabolism of the cell. Nothing, however, is known about its origin and reproduction except by analogy with the cortex of ciliates. Some workers believe that the cell membrane is connected with the endoplasmic reticulum, just as this is continuous with the nuclear membrane, as shown in Fig. 1.1. It has also been claimed that there are interconnections between these membranes and the membranes of mitochondria and plastids, but it is too early to judge the significance of these claims.

None of the structures included in this brief survey of the lesser known extrachromosomal cell constituents is known to possess physical continuity. Nevertheless their permanence, widespread distribution, and essential role in cell metabolism make them the likeliest additions to the list of cell constituents that, like centrioles, kinetosomes, plastids, and mitochondria, show physical continuity from one cell generation to another.

References

Brachet, Jean, *Biochemical Cytology*. New York: Academic Press, Inc., 1957.

Granick, Sam, "Plastid Structure, Development, and Inheritance," *Encyclopedia of Plant Physiology* (1955), I, 507.

Picken, L. E. R., *The Organization of Cells and Other Organisms*. New York: Oxford University Press, 1960.

Questions

2.1. What is the evidence for the homology of centrioles and basal granules?

2.2. What is the essential difference between reproduction of an extrachromosomal element by fission and by generation? How does this difference affect our criteria for recognizing the physical continuity of an extrachromosomal element?

Three

Genetic Continuity
of Extrachromosomal Structures

While a cytological demonstration of the physical continuity of an extrachromosomal cell constituent establishes a prima-facie case for regarding it as a bearer of hereditary information, it is not in itself conclusive. Evidence of genetic continuity is still required. A prerequisite for demonstrating genetic continuity is the occurrence of a mutation that causes a phenotypic change. The phenotypic change must then be followed through successive generations, following a cross to a contrasting phenotype. If, in these generations, an invariable association can be demonstrated between the mutant phenotype and a structurally or functionally altered extrachromosomal entity, and it can further be shown that the transmission of the mutant phenotype from one generation to the next is in the manner expected if the hereditary determinant were borne on the extrachromosomal entity, it may then be inferred that the latter possesses genetic continuity.

Thus a rather involved combination of cytological observation and experimental breeding is required to demonstrate not only that an extrachromosomal entity possesses physical continuity, but that this continuity extends to any alteration in the hereditary information it carries. This rigorous program has rarely, if ever, been carried out for a single instance of extrachromosomal inheritance. However, the cumulative evidence from independent occurrences of extrachromosomal heredity, all implicating the same extrachromosomal cell constituents, leaves little doubt that they are the bearers of hereditary information.

The prime difficulty in demonstrating genetic continuity of extrachromosomal entities is that, since they are so important for the proper functioning of cell division and cell metabolism, their loss or the loss of their function must be lethal except in special circumstances. For example, a plant without chloroplasts or with functionally useless chloroplasts cannot photosynthesize, and hence must die. Changed phenotypes such as these, therefore, can only be studied in *Euglena*, where photosynthesis is not necessary for life, or in chimaeras, where only part of a plant suffers the loss and can rely on the remainder of the plant for the products of photosynthesis. Similarly, a loss or change in function of the mitochondria can be tolerated only in an organism such as yeast, where there is an efficient anaerobic alternative to aerobic respiration. And, lacking an organism where the function of the centrioles is dispensable, an experimental investigation of their genetic continuity must be derived from their homology with the kinetosomes of the ciliates, which may be lost or gained without killing these organisms.

Bearing this initial limitation in mind, let us examine the evidence for the genetic continuity of extrachromosomal entities. Since a general account of the breeding behavior of extrachromosomally inherited differences is given in Chapters 4, 5, and 6, their contribution to the demonstrations of genetic continuity will be only briefly touched upon here.

Fiber-producers

In the ciliates, *Paramecium aurelia* in particular, mutant phenotypes with duplications and deficiencies in certain cortical structures are known. These mutants are often permanent, surviving repeated multiplication in vegetative reproduction. As already mentioned, these mutants differ from the normal in the duplication or absence of particular groups of kinetosomes. There is an invariable association between a particular mutant phenotype and the presence or absence of particular groups of kinetosomes.

Extensive crosses between mutant forms and normal individuals have been performed by Tracy M. Sonneborn and R. V. Dippell. In *P. aurelia*, crosses are effectively consummated only between animals of opposite mating types but of the same variety. Individuals of different mating types pair and become attached in the region of the mouth. Since some of the mutant phenotypes in these crosses have two mouths, one such mutant will pair simultaneously with two normal individuals of the appropriate mating type.

Cytological and genetic data have elucidated the behavior of the chromosomal material during mating (Fig. 3.1). In *Paramecium*, the chromosomal material is organized into two distinct types of nuclei, the micro- and the macro-, which are the germ and somatic nuclei

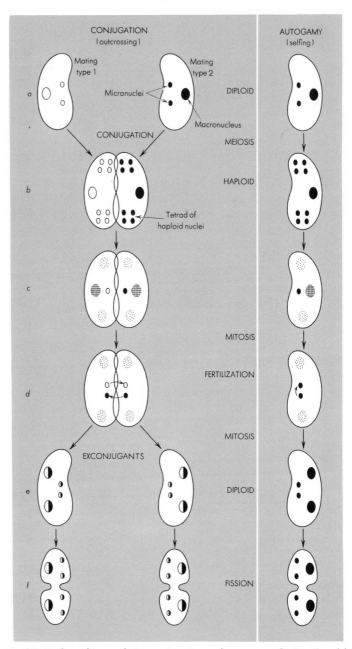

Fig. 3.1. Nuclear changes during conjugation and autogamy. *Conjugation:* (a)
Two parental animals from the same variety, but belonging to different mating
types, each with one macronucleus and two diploid micronuclei. (b) The animals
pair, and each micronucleus undergoes meiosis to give four haploid nuclei. (c)
Seven of the haploid nuclei in each conjugant disintegrate, and the macronucleus breaks up. (d) The remaining haploid nucleus in each conjugant divides
mitotically; one nucleus, the migratory, moves into its mate where it fuses with
the other, the stationary, nucleus. (e) Each fusion nucleus divides twice mitotically. Two products give rise to the macronuclei, and the other two become
new micronuclei. (f) A mitotic division of the micronuclei, accompanied by
fission, initiates an exconjugant clone in which each animal once more contains

respectively. The micronuclei, of which there are two, are diploid. During meiosis each micronucleus produces four haploid nuclei, seven of which disintegrate. The remaining nucleus by a further mitotic division produces the two gamete nuclei, one of which is stationary; the other—the migratory—passes into the cytoplasm of its mate. Thus there is a reciprocal exchange of a migratory nucleus between mates, followed by the fusion of the newly entered migratory nucleus and the stationary nucleus to restore the diploid complement. The chromosomal content of the mates at the end of fertilization is obviously identical.

During this process the single macronucleus is disintegrating, to be replaced by two of the four nuclei produced by two mitotic divisions of the newly formed diploid nucleus. The other two become the micronuclei. The complete sequence of nuclear changes is shown diagrammatically in Fig. 3.1.

After fertilization, each mate, now called an exconjugant, produces a clone of animals by binary fission. For every chromosomally determined difference that originally distinguished the mates, the two exconjugant clones are identically heterozygous. The first significant observation is, therefore, that in matings between the double and normal paramecia, the clone derived from the mutant exconjugant consists of only mutant animals and the clone derived from the normal exconjugant consists of only normal animals (Fig. 3.3). Therefore, the hereditary determinant controlling this difference cannot be chromosomally borne.

This conclusion is supported by a further observation. Single individuals of *Paramecium* may undergo a process of nuclear reorganization known as autogamy, the consequences of which are equivalent to self-fertilization (Fig. 3.2). Autogamy can be induced by starving animals that have been previously supplied with excess food. The nuclear behavior is identical with that preceding crossing, except that two nuclei from the same animal fuse instead of two from different animals. Since the two nuclei that fuse are mitotic products of the same haploid nucleus, all the animals that have undergone autogamy become homozygous. Thus if a clone of animals that are heterozygous at a single locus (*Aa*) undergo autogamy, they will become homozygous for one or the other of the two alleles at this locus (*AA* or *aa*) with about equal frequencies. Hence there is segregation for all genes for which an exconjugant is heterozygous. There is no segregation, following autogamy, of exconjugants of matings between double and normal animals (Fig. 3.3). It follows, therefore, that the exconjugants cannot be heterozygous for genes controlling the difference between double and normal animals, from which it can be inferred that the double and normal animals themselves cannot differ by any chromosomal genes.

one macronucleus and two micronuclei. All the nuclei are heterozygous at every locus for which the initial parents carried different alleles. *Autogamy:* All stages are identical with conjugation, except that only one animal is involved; hence the two mitotic nuclei at stage *d* fuse to give the fusion nucleus of stage *e*. After G. H. Beale, *The Genetics of Paramecium aurelia* (Cambridge University Press, 1954).

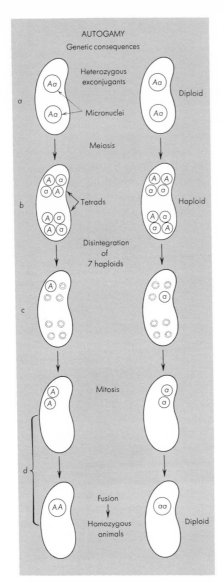

Fig. 3.2. Gene segregation at autogamy. Stages *a-d* correspond to those of Fig. 3.1, but only the micronuclei are shown for clarity. The two possible results of autogamy in an exconjugant clone that is heterozygous at a single locus are shown. Since the fusion nucleus is derived from two mitotic products of the same nucleus, it is always homozygous at all loci. However, since the surviving haploid nucleus (stages *b* and *c*) is chosen at random out of the eight available, the fusion nucleus will be as frequently homozygous for one allele as for the other. Based on Tracy M. Sonneborn, "Recent Advances in the Genetics of *Paramecium* and *Euplotes*," *Advan. Genet., 1* (1947).

This suggests an extrachromosomal site for the hereditary determinant of this difference in phenotype.

But in *Paramecium* a further possibility must first be considered, namely, a chromosomal control exerted through the macronucleus rather than the micronucleus. The usual situation is for the micronucleus and the macronucleus to have identical gene contents, since they are derived from mitotic products of a single nucleus and hence their respective contributions to the cell phenotype are indistinguishable. Sonneborn, however, has described animals that, following mating or autogamy, develop a new macronucleus not from the fusion nucleus but from some of the disintegrating fragments of the old macronucleus.

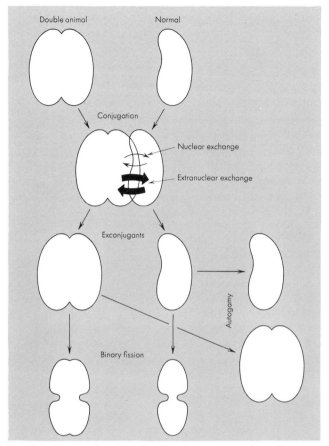

Fig. 3.3. The results of conjugation between double and normal animals, followed by autogamy among the exconjugants. The results are the same, whether or not there is exchange of mobile extranuclear material during conjugation. Reference to Figs. 3.1 and 3.2 will show that these results could not occur if the difference between the double and normal animals were under gene control. Based on Tracy M. Sonneborn and R. V. Dippell, "The Modes of Replication of Cortical Organizers in *Paramecium aurelia*, Syngen 4," *Genetics*, 46 (1961).

This process occurs sporadically under normal conditions, but more regularly at 38°C. When it occurs, the macronucleus has a gene content appropriate to the previous generation. Thus autogamy of heterozygous animals followed by macronuclear regeneration yields an animal whose micronuclei are homozygous and whose macronucleus is still heterozygous. By this type of manipulation, Sonneborn was able to make many comparisons of animals whose micronuclei had one gene content and whose macronuclei had another. From these comparisons he found that the cell phenotype was generally under the control of genes in the macronucleus. The same type of manipulation, however, has failed to demonstrate any macronuclear control of the difference between double and normal animals. This difference is, therefore, strictly extrachromosomal in origin.

Which part of the extrachromosomal system is responsible? In some stocks, no substantial exchange of extrachromosomal material occurs between mates during a normal mating. In others, the cytoplasmic bridge connecting mates may persist after fertilization, and as a result considerable exchange of extrachromosomal material occurs. Any difference in the mobile extrachromosomal cell complement of the mates is thereby averaged out. Genetic and cytological proof of this will be presented later. For the present, it is sufficient to note that a free exchange of extrachromosomal material between double and normal animals during mating does not affect the outcome of the mating. The difference, therefore, cannot reside in the mobile extrachromosomal fraction. Hence by a process of elimination the hereditary control has been localized in the rigid cortical ectoplasm.

In conclusion, cytological evidence suggests that the cortex possesses physical continuity, which probably resides in its kinetosomes. Cytological observations and breeding experiments show an invariable association between an abnormal cortical and kinety pattern and a mutant phenotype. Finally, the breeding experiments show that the transmission of the mutant phenotype from one generation to the next following a cross to a normal phenotype is only compatible with the hereditary determinants being located in the cortex. That is, some constituent of the cortex possesses genetic continuity. This constituent is either the kinetosomes or some entity that profoundly affects the behavior of the kinetosomes. In the light of the cumulative evidence from other organisms and the homology between kinetosomes and centrioles, the former alternative seems more likely.

Mitochondria

Evidence for the genetic continuity of the mitochondrion comes exclusively from observations on certain slow-growing mutants of fungi. Extensive breeding experiments, as well as numerous ancillary observations, leave no doubt that the difference in phenotype between each of these mutants and the normal is extrachromosomal in origin. But the results of these crosses, which are presented in Chapter 4, do not identify any extrachromosomal entity in particular.

Cytological and biochemical observations appear to narrow the possible extrachromosomal entities to the mitochondrion. Recent electron microscopic studies on the mitochondria of slow-growing yeast cells have detected structural abnormalities. Similar studies with *Neurospora* have shown that for many hours after the germination of asexual spores produced by a colony of a slow-growing mutant there are few if any normal mitochondria present—only a mass of unorganized double-membrane material. However, there are also strong indications that this represents only an extension of what is normally a short transitory stage of the germination of all asexual spores. Hence there may be a slowing down of the normal development of the mitochondria rather than a permanent change in their structure.

The cells of the slow-growing (petite) cultures of yeast have lost their aerobic respiratory mechanism. The characteristic slow growth of the petite mutants is a direct consequence of this respiratory defect. The difference in the rate of growth of normal and petite cells disappears in the absence of oxygen. Petite cells, unlike normal cells, are

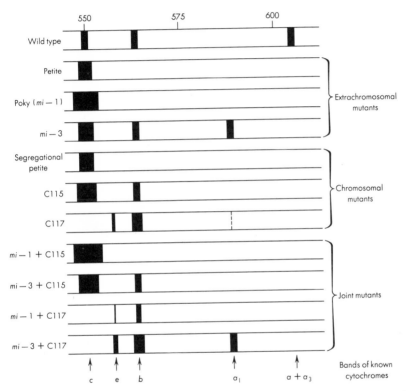

Fig. 3.4. The absorption bands of the cytochromes of normal and mutant strains of yeast and *Neurospora*. The wider the band, the higher the concentration. The positions of the bands of known cytochromes are shown for comparison. From R. P. Wagner and Herschel Mitchell, *Genetics and Metabolism* (John Wiley & Sons, 1955).

insensitive to respiratory poisons such as cyanides. The respiratory defect of the mutants is attributable to the simultaneous absence of several respiratory enzymes, namely, cytochrome oxidase, cytochrome-c reductase, and cytochrome a and b (Fig. 3.4). All these enzymes are known to be carried in the normal cell by the mitochondria. Hence it can be concluded that the mitochondria of petite cells are functionally defective.

In *Neurospora*, some aerobic respiration is vital for survival. However, there are many similarities between the situation just described for yeast and that found in the slow-growing poky and other *mi* variants of *Neurospora*. The respiration of poky is defective, but the oxygen uptake is still one-third normal. Old cells, but not young ones, are sensitive to cyanide. Poky, like petite, lacks cytochromes *a* and *b*. Both have an excess of cytochrome *c*, although this excess is much greater in poky (Fig. 3.4). During the growth of a poky colony, however, the mitochondria change in composition and in the activity of the succinoxidase system. As the colony ages, the activity of the latter becomes more nearly normal. Similarly, the level of cytochrome oxidase increases with age but never reaches more than half the normal activity. In contrast, the succinic dehydrogenase level is essentially normal in poky at all ages.

Compared with petite, poky has two outstanding properties. First, it is a less extreme variant, containing reduced levels of many enzymes that are completely lacking in petite; second, its enzyme content becomes more normal with age. This second property suggests, as did the cytological evidence, that there is a retardation of development in poky rather than a complete failure, as found in petite. Thus there is about as close an agreement between the cytological and biochemical properties of petite and poky as might be expected, if we bear in mind their differing degrees of dependence on the aerobic respiratory system. Combined, they constitute a formidable argument for the genetic continuity of the mitochondrion.

On the other hand, while the petite and poky variants demonstrate an invariable association between an extrachromosomally inherited difference in phenotype and structural and functional differences in the mitochondrion, single chromosomal gene mutations are known, both in yeast and in *Neurospora*, that produce similar upsets in the respiratory enzymes of the mitochondrion (Fig. 3.4.). In these chromosomally inherited examples, the changes in the mitochondria are clearly the result of changes in hereditary material situated outside the mitochondria. This being so, there seems no reason why the abnormal mitochondria of petite and poky should not also be the result of changes in extrachromosomal hereditary material other than the mitochondria themselves. The genetic continuity might reside not in the mitochondria but in some other extrachromosomal entity that partly controls their phenotype. This is always a possible alternative explanation for the types of observations that have been made so far in support of the genetic continuity of every recognizable extrachromosomal entity. This alternative has only been successfully ruled out in certain cases of plastid inheritance.

Plastids

Historically, the plastids were the subject of the first case of alleged genetic continuity of an extrachromosomal cell constituent. In almost every plant species, albino variants or variegated individuals possessing albino sectors are known. Their plastids have lost the capacity to produce chlorophyll, or they have lost all recognizable plastids. A completely albino plant is, of course, lethal; it invariably dies while it is still a seedling. If albino tissues arise by mutation during the growth of a plant, however, the regular separation of layers in development confines the albino tissue to certain regions where they are maintained by photosynthetic products of neighboring normal tissues. The germ cells are derived from the subepidermal layer. If, therefore, any part of this layer is albino, the mutant cells can be bred from it, and the inheritance of this condition determined.

In many instances, the changed structure or function of the plastids is inherited as a single chromosomal gene mutant. In maize alone, many mutant genes are known that produce a phenotypic effect on the plastids, but in many other cases the inheritance is non-Mendelian, and is only explicable in terms of the genetic continuity of an extrachromosomal entity. The first example of this kind was discovered by C. Correns while he was working with green-white variegated plants of *Mirabilis jalopa*. He found that, irrespective of the pollen parent, flowers on the green sectors of the plant gave only green progeny and flowers on the white sectors gave only white progeny. Flowers on the variegated branches gave mixed progeny, with green, white, and variegated seedlings in widely differing ratios.

The simplest and most widely accepted interpretation of these and numerous similar observations is that due to E. Baur. It assumes that variegated plants possess two distinct kinds of plastids, normal and mutant. Normal plastids arise by multiplication of the normal plastids, mutants by multiplication of the mutant plastids. Starting from an ovule with both types of plastid, multiplication and segregation at mitotic cell divisions produce some cells that possess only mutant plastids, others only normal plastids, and others mixed plastids. In *M. jalopa* these plastids would produce respectively white sectors, normal green sectors, and variegated sectors capable of further sectoring.

The critical observation for the acceptance of this explanation is of cells containing both normal and mutant plastids. As mentioned in Chapter 2, mixed cells whose normal and abnormal plastids were apparently self-perpetuating have been observed in the alga *Spirogyra triformis*. In *Primula sinensis*, a maternally transmitted variegation has been described by R. P. Gregory. The green parts contained normal plastids, the white parts contained smaller, almost colorless plastids, and the meristematic cells, which produced both types of cell, contained both types of plastid. Mixed cells have also been reported for an extrachromosomally inherited variegation in *Nepeta cataria*. M. W. Woods and H. G. Du Buy reported at least fifteen distinct plastid mutants, some of which were almost normal while others were deficient in pigment and had various morphological abnormalities, in plants homozygous for the recessive chromosomal gene *m*.

In the examples above, as in others described by E. Baur in *Pelargonium zonale*, there is a certain (usually low) degree of pollen transmission of the entity that controls the plastid phenotype. In *N. cataria*, pollen of variegated plants crossed to normal green mothers may give as many as 27 per cent variegated progeny. What is more important, a pollen parent with a morphologically distinct type of abnormal plastid, when crossed to a normal mother, gave progeny in which the same abnormal plastid could be recognized in as many as 24 per cent of the plants.

Mixed cells are by no means always found. For example, they have never been demonstrated in the many instances of extrachromosomally inherited variegation in maize. Similarly, Correns found that mixed cells were too rare for Baur's interpretation to be generally valid (but see Chapter 8). He therefore proposed the alternative explanation that the plastid changes were secondary effects of heritable cytoplasmic differences that permit or inhibit plastid development. That is, he attributed the genetic continuity to an extrachromosomal entity other than the plastid.

An important factor in this controversy is undoubtedly that the ease with which mixed cells may be recognized varies enormously from one species to another and from one mutant form of the plastid to another. Furthermore, the stage in the development of the cells at the time of making the observations can be critical. There is no doubt, for example, that variation in the stage of development or degeneration of the plastids within a cell can give the appearance of a mixed cell. Nevertheless, many observers, fully aware of these difficulties, insist that mixed cells can be regularly observed in variegated plants.

These points are well illustrated by a survey of 172 variegated mutants of *Epilobium* carried out by Peter Michaelis. Among these mutants, fifty had demonstrable mixed cells; thirty had no mixed cells; and, in the remaining ninety-two, mixed cells could not be established because the difference between the mutant and normal form of the plastid was too small. In another instance, described by Marcus M. Rhoades, the difference between the mutant and normal form of the plastid is very great, and cells containing only one or the other form are apparently easy to score; the mutant form, however, is so minute that it is virtually impossible to rule out its presence in cells that appear to contain only normal plastids.

Another line of evidence for the genetic continuity of plastids comes from quite a different type of observation, namely, the exhaustive survey of species crosses in *Oenothera*. These were started by O. Renner and continued by W. Stubbe, H. T. Stinson, and R. E. Cleland. (See Chapters 4 and 11.) One typical example, involving reciprocal crosses between *O. muricata* and *O. Hookeri*, illustrates the general result (Fig. 3.5). *O. muricata*, like many *Oenothera* species, is a complex permanent heterozygote. (In *Oenothera* species, special genetic mechanisms—for example, balanced lethals—permit heterozygotes to breed true.) It produces two kinds of gamete known as *curvans* and *rigens;* most of the male gametes are of the former kind, and most of the female gametes are of the latter kind. But from both reciprocal crosses with *O. Hookeri* the same hybrid gene complex or genome, known as *ʰHookeri-curvans*, can be obtained, and it is only this portion of the reciprocal progenies that we shall consider further. If *O. Hookeri* is the mother of the *ʰHookeri-curvans* hybrid it is yellow

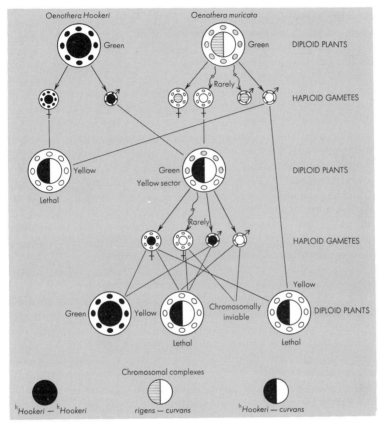

Fig. 3.5. The consequences of reciprocally crossing *Oenothera Hookeri* and *O. muricata*. The latter produces two kinds of gametes, *rigens* and *curvans*. Most male gametes are of the latter kind and most female gametes are of the former. Identical genomes, *ʰHookeri-curvans*, can be obtained from both reciprocal crosses, and only the phenotypes and breeding behavior of these are represented. The diagram shows how the plastids of *O. Hookeri* retain their capacity to function normally in collaboration with the *ʰHookeri* genome, even after one or more generations of abnormal function when in combination with the hybrid genome. It also shows that the yellow sectors of the *O. muricata* plastid-hybrid genome combination are due to paternal plastids. Based on O. Renner, "Zur Kenntnis der nichtmendelnden Buntheit der Laubblätter," *Flora (Jena),* **30** (1936).

and soon dies, whereas if *O. muricata* is the mother the hybrid is green and normal. The latter, nevertheless, develops yellow sectors whose appearance is like that of the reciprocal cross. This can be interpreted to mean that the mother provides most of the plastids of the hybrid and that, although the plastids provided by *O. Hookeri* cannot function with the *^{h}Hookeri-curvans* genome, those provided by *O. muricata* can. Hence the abnormal plastids that produce the yellow sectors must, according to this interpretation, be *O. Hookeri* plastids brought in by the pollen parent.

This interpretation can be tested, because in some instances flowers arise on the sectors containing the putative *O. Hookeri* plastids. When self-pollinated, these flowers give two kinds of progeny, *^{h}Hookeri-curvans*, which are all yellow and therefore die, and *^{h}Hookeri-^{h}Hookeri*, which are all normal green. Similarly, when these flowers are back-crossed with *O. muricata* pollen, all the progeny are of the yellow, lethal *^{h}Hookeri-curvans* type, while backcrossing with *O. Hookeri* pollen gives the normal green *^{h}Hookeri-^{h}Hookeri* types only. Thus the plastids of the yellow sectors behave as though they are of the *Hookeri* type; they are yellow with the hybrid gene complex and green with the pure *Hookeri* genome. Thus the interpretation is proved correct.

What is more important, in this reaction between the plastids and the genome, is that both components are equally permanent and autonomous. The function of the plastids was upset in a foreign genome, but the plastids themselves remained unaffected when recombined with their own genome. Even after plastids had been exposed in this way to a foreign genome for fourteen consecutive generations, they produced the normal phenotype when they were reassociated with their own genome; the long association had produced no detectable change in them. This is surely the most dramatic demonstration of the genetic continuity of an extrachromosomal cell constituent.

The plastids of *O. muricata* and *O. Hookeri* are demonstrably different in their reaction to an identical genome, and their differences persist undiminished by their association with a foreign genome. This implies permanent, heritable differences between the plastids of these two species, a conclusion that applies equally well to the many other pairs of species that Renner and others have studied. The plastid differences could have arisen only during or after the separation of the species, which now constitute this genus. It cannot be doubted, therefore, that plastids may change by mutation or that the changed forms are capable of self-perpetuation. Hence two important assumptions in Baur's interpretation of extrachromosomally inherited variegations are proved. The other assumption, namely, the occurrence of mixed cells, has been satisfied in a number of instances.

For reasons enumerated above, the demonstration of mixed cells is more critical than the failures to find them. Baur's interpretation, which involves the genetic continuity of the plastids, is, therefore, more acceptable than the alternative on the present evidence. On the other hand, there is no reason why the different mechanisms proposed by Baur and Correns should be regarded as mutually exclusive explanations of variegation. The experiments just described show that chromosomal and plastid control of the phenotype of the latter are quite compatible. This leaves no grounds, therefore, for rejecting an extrachromosomal control of the plastid phenotype in addition to that exercised by the plastids themselves. Rather, a multiple control of the phenotype of the individual components might be expected in the highly integrated system that is a cell. Indeed the permissible level of independent variation of the parts of a cell must be limited by the requirements for successful cooperation.

The foregoing survey of the main lines of evidence for the genetic continuity of recognizable extrachromosomal cellular constituents has not exhausted the evidence for the genetic continuity of extrachromosomal entities, whose existence has so far been deduced solely from breeding experiments. These will be described in the following chapters.

References

Cleland, R. E., "The Cytogenetics of *Oenothera*," *Advan. Genet., 11* (1962), 147.

Ephrussi, Boris, *Nucleo-cytoplasmic Relations in Micro-Organisms.* New York: Oxford University Press, 1953.

Rhoades, Marcus M., "Interaction of Genic and Non-genic Hereditary Units and the Physiology of Non-genic Inheritance," *Encyclopedia of Plant Physiology* (1955), I, 19.

Wettstein, Ditter von, "Nuclear and Cytoplasmic Factors in Development of Chloroplast Structure and Function," *Can. J. Botany, 39* (1961), 1537.

Questions

3.1. Why is the occurrence of cells containing both mutant and normal plastids critical for the plastogene theory of plastid variegations in plants?

3.2. The cytology, biochemistry, and inheritance of the petite variant of yeast prove that plasmagenes contribute to the structure and function of mitochondria but do not prove the genetic continuity of mitochondria. Discuss this statement.

Four

Differences between Reciprocal Crosses

The extrachromosomal basis of a heritable difference in phenotype is inferred from the failure of this difference to be transmitted from parent to offspring in the manner expected of a chromosomally controlled difference. Thus extrachromosomal inheritance is defined and detected as an exception to Mendelian inheritance. In practice, the breeding tests for extrachromosomal inheritance are largely a step-by-step elimination of all possible chromosomal explanations of the observed behavior. Unfortunately, non-Mendelian inheritance may result from many novel chromosomal phenomena whose number and variety are constantly being added to, with a corresponding increase in the difficulty of establishing extrachromosomal heredity. As a consequence, there has been a constant proliferation of tests in an attempt to maintain rigorous proofs of extrachromosomal transmission. Some of these are of general applicability, while others exploit special features of a particular life cycle or a restricted experimental technique. Underlying them all are a few basic genetic principles.

Chromosomally inherited differences

In general, it is quite unimportant for the transmission of a chromosomally borne gene whether it comes from the male or female parent or whether it goes into a male or female gamete. Therefore, where strains differ only by chromosomal genes, the progeny of reciprocal crosses between them—that is, crosses in which the source of male and female gametes are reversed—are generally identical in phenotype. Furthermore, all later generations derived from the initial reciprocal crosses are not affected by the direction in which the original cross was made. This rule, which was first noted by Gregor Mendel, holds for all hereditary characters determined by chromosomal genes; the only regular exception is due to sex-linked genes. Since the pattern of the inheritance of the latter is quite characteristic and predictable, its recognition presents few problems. (See Franklin W. Stahl's *The Mechanics of Inheritance,* another volume in this series.) And in the plant kingdom sex linkage is, in any case, extremely rare.

Irregular exceptions to the equality of reciprocal crosses are also known. These exceptions usually result from preferential segregation of chromosomes during gametogenesis. The orientation of the two homologous chromosomes of a bivalent with respect to the two spindle poles around which the new daughter nuclei will form is usually at random, as is also the orientation of the different bivalents with respect to one another. If this were not so, Mendel's laws would not hold for the genes they bore. A number of cases have been reported, however, in which nonrandom segregation occurs, in that a particular chromosome preferentially passes to a specific pole. The consequences of this are seen during the production of the female gametes. In oogenesis, only one of the four haploid chromosome complements produced by meiosis becomes the egg pronucleus; the other three pass into nonfunctional polar bodies. In megasporogenesis, usually only one of the four megaspores develops into the embryo sac. It follows, therefore, that the chromosome preferentially segregated to the spindle pole (from which the functional egg or megaspore nucleus was derived) would be present in the majority of female gametes. Preferential segregation, however, does not affect the constitution of the male gametes. All the haploid products of meiosis contribute equally to the chromosome complements of sperm and pollen, irrespective of which spindle pole they segregate to during spermatogenesis or microsporogenesis. Hence the frequency of transmission of genes borne on a preferentially segregating chromosome is no longer independent of whether it comes from the male or female parent. It follows, therefore, that the progeny of reciprocal crosses can differ for genes borne on such a chromosome, since reversing the source of male and female gametes will now affect the genotype of the resulting progenies.

A chromosome that shows preferential segregation varies; it may be an abnormal homologue of the normal chromosome complement, for example, abnormal chromosome ten in maize, or it may be additional to the normal complement, that is, a so-called accessory or B chromosome. Similarly, the cause of their preferential segregation appears to vary, but this need not concern us here. The only fact that matters is that the preferential segregation can only operate in the special conditions characterizing egg and megaspore formation.

Maternal nutrition

If sex linkage and preferential segregation are ruled out (and they often can be, either on a priori grounds or as a result of cytological observations and breeding tests), then differences between reciprocal crosses are prospectively indicative of extrachromosomal inheritance. In higher organisms, however, the offspring is retained by the mother, who feeds and protects it during early growth and development. The offspring of reciprocal crosses are thus subjected to different maternal environments during this sensitive period of development, and the phenotypes of reciprocal crosses may differ for this reason alone. Similarly, differences may also arise where the early nutrition and protection of the embryo depend on materials, such as yolks and shells, that are provided solely by the maternal parent. Thus even if the contributions of mother and father to the genome and plasmon of the offspring were equal, the mother, because of her special contribution to the early development of the embryo, might still exert a greater influence on its phenotype. This influence, if effective, would be expected in general to make the phenotype of the offspring more like that of the strain from which the mother was taken. That is, it would be expected to result in maternal inheritance. A maternal inheritance that depends solely on differences in the maternal environment in which the embryo develops or on differences in the nutrients supplied to the egg is, however, transient. It will disappear within one generation or it will appear with a diminishing effect in the successive generations derived from the initial reciprocal crosses. Clearly, if differences between reciprocal crosses are to be used as a criterion of extrachromosomal heredity, we must specify that the difference persists undiminished through the successive generations that may be derived from them. What now remains to be considered is why extrachromosomal heredity might be expected to lead to differences between reciprocal crosses.

Persistent differences

Reciprocal differences result only where the two sexes make unequal contributions to the offspring. To be persistent, such a difference must involve an unequal contribution of hereditary determinants. Therefore, for a persistent difference to result from extrachromosomal inheritance, the two sexes must make unequal contributions of extrachromosomally borne plasmagenes. Differences in the quantity of extrachromosomal material contained in the gametes of the two sexes are the rule rather than the exception, the gametes of the female being the larger.

If there is any inequality, it will be the female gamete that will contribute the greater part of the extrachromosomal heredity material; the result, in general, will therefore be maternal inheritance. It would be wrong, however, automatically to equate quantity of extrachromosomal material with quality. For some extrachromosomal entities, the smaller contribution of the male gamete might be as important or more important than the larger contribution of the female gamete. Indeed, we have already seen that in *Amphibia* the centriole contributed by the sperm may be the only one that is functional in the zygote. We cannot exclude the possibility, therefore, that paternal inheritance is also indicative of extrachromosomal heredity. Nor can we expect all extrachromosomally inherited differences to result in differences between the progenies of reciprocal crosses.

Persistent differences between reciprocal crosses that have been ascribed to extrachromosomal inheritance have been found in plants and in animals. These differences between the reciprocal crosses are basically of two kinds: those in which the difference is due to some degree of maternal inheritance, and those in which the difference is due to the appearance of a novel phenotype when the cross is made in one direction but not in the other.

Plastid differences

The most extensively investigated class of variants showing maternal transmission is that of the plastid chimaeras of higher plants. Some of their properties have already been discussed in Chapter 3, but a few aspects of their breeding behavior should be examined in detail as a model of this kind of inheritance.

In some species—for example, *Mirabilis jalopa, Primula sinensis, Zea mays,* and *Antirrhinum*—reciprocal crosses between normal plants or normal branches of variegated plants and branches with abnormal plastids result in exclusive maternal determination of the progeny. The normal mother gives only normal progeny, the abnormal mother only abnormal progeny, irrespective of the phenotype of the male parent (Fig. 4.1). We may infer, therefore, a corresponding exclusively maternal transmission of the plastogenes or plasmagenes that control this difference in phenotype. In other species, some members of the genus *Epilobium,* for example, the maternal transmission is not quite exclusive (see Fig. 3.5). Peter Michaelis found that three in every thousand progeny from a cross between a female with normal plastids and a male with abnormal plastids contained sectors with abnormal plastids. Their determinants were presumably brought in by the male gamete. Similarly, in crosses between species of *Oenothera,* male transmission of plastids is responsible for the occurrence of sectors containing the plastids of the paternal species (see Chapters 3 and 5). Nevertheless, in both *Epilobium* and *Oenothera,* the male transmission is relatively trivial. This, however, is not always the case. In *Nepeta cataria,* as many as 27 per cent of the progeny of a cross may be variegated chimaeras containing plastids with both the maternal and paternal phenotypes. A high level of male transmission is also found in *Pelargonium zonale,* where 30 per cent of the progeny from a cross between a mother with abnormal plastids and a father with normal plastids are variegated, possessing both normal and abnormal plastids.

In the reciprocal cross, **70** per cent possess the abnormal plastids of the pollen parent; when the cross is made in this direction, some of the progeny possess *only* plastids with the paternal phenotype.

Thus within the flowering plants can be found examples ranging from exclusively maternal to approximately equal maternal and paternal transmission of the determinants that control the phenotype of the plastids. An important conclusion can therefore be drawn from the inheritance of plastid differences: although persistent differences

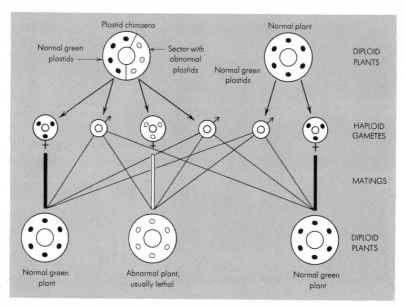

Fig. 4.1. Maternal inheritance in a cross between a plastid chimaera and a normal plant. In this example, the plastid phenotype of the progeny is determined solely by that of the maternal parent.

between reciprocal crosses may be a general property of many examples of extrachromosomal inheritance, *exclusive* maternal inheritance is not.

Male sterility

Male sterility due to pollen failure is widespread among flowering plants. Male-sterile mutants have been found in most crop plants. Their inheritance is of two kinds: first, there are those that are inherited as single, recessive, chromosomal genes; second, there are those that show maternal inheritance. One of the earliest and most fully investigated examples of the latter (Fig. 4.2), was described by Marcus M. Rhoades, who obtained a male-sterile line of *Zea mays* that, when crossed to pollen from any normal line, gave more or less exclusively male-sterile offspring. Repeated backcrossing of the male-sterile line to lines with fertile pollen did not restore fertility, even after the backcrossing had resulted in the complete substitution of all the chromosomes of the fertile line for those of the male-sterile line. Thus not only did male sterility show persistent maternal transmission, but no chromosomal male-sterility factors could be demonstrated.

Further analysis was made possible by the occasional production of a little pollen by plants of the male-sterile line. This allowed reciprocal

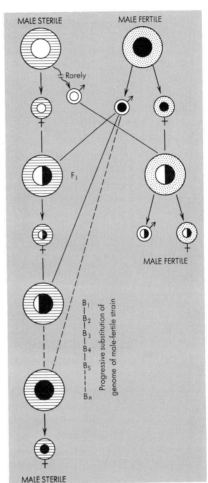

Fig. 4.2. Maternal inheritance of male sterility. The occasional production of a small amount of pollen by the male-sterile line allows reciprocal crosses to be made, and these reveal the strict maternal transmission. Complete substitution of the genome of the male-sterile line by repeated backcrossing to a normal line as the pollen parent does not restore the male fertility. Based on Marcus M. Rhoades, "The Cytoplasmic Inheritance of Male Sterility in Zea mays," *J. Genet.,* 27 (1933).

crossing with male-fertile lines that showed that predominantly maternal transmission occurred irrespective of the direction in which the cross was made. Since neither cytological investigation nor extensive breeding tests, employing lines carrying known genes on all chromosomes, gave any evidence of preferential segregation or of any other type of abnormal segregation of chromosomal material, Rhoades concluded that his example of male sterility was controlled by plasmagenes, which are usually transmitted mainly by the female gametes. Similar examples are now commonplace, not only in maize but also in many other related and unrelated species throughout the flowering plants.

Maternal inheritance in *Neurospora*

Virtually exclusively maternal inheritance is also found for poky and other members of the *mi* series of variants of the fungus *Neurospora crassa* (see Chapter 3). In this heterothallic ascomycete there are two mating types, *A* and *a*, and reciprocal crosses are possible between them because both can be used as a maternal (protoperithecial) and a paternal (conidial) parent (Fig. 4.3). The haploid vegetative mycelium of both mating types produce protoperithecia and conidia, and fertilization is achieved by bringing the conidia of one mating type into contact with the protoperithecia of the other. The protoperithecial parent provides the bulk of the extrachromosomal material of the resulting diploid zygote. Hence it also provides the bulk of the extrachromosomal contents of the haploid sexual spores (ascospores) produced by the zygote, and all the nutritional requirements of the sexual reproductive cycle as well. Germination of the ascospores to produce a new generation of haploid vegetative mycelia completes the life cycle.

In reciprocal crosses between three of the *mi* series of variants and a normal colony, Herschel K. Mitchell and Mary B. Mitchell found that the phenotype of the progeny was the same as that of the protoperithecial parent; the only exception was that in the cross involving the normal conidial parent 0.1 per cent of the progeny were normal (Fig. 4.3). The phenotypes of the progeny were retained through successive crosses, in which they were the protoperithecial parent, and through indefinite periods of vegetative growth. Persistent protoperithecial transmission of another variant of *N. crassa*, called "slow growth" (SG), has been described by Adrian M. Srb. If SG is crossed as the protoperithecial parent to a normal strain, all the progeny have the SG phenotype. If the latter are again crossed by conidia of a normal strain, the result is the same for eighteen consecutive backcrosses without any change in the composition of the progeny.

In *Neurospora*, as in most ascomycetes, the diploid zygotic nucleus undergoes meiosis to produce four haploid nuclei. Each of these divides mitotically to provide the haploid nuclei of the eight ascospores produced by each zygote. All eight ascospores are contained in a sac (ascus). The zygote is heterozygous for every chromosomal gene for which the parents differ. Hence four of the eight ascospores in each ascus will contain the allele contributed by one parent to the zygote, and four will contain the allele contributed by the other parent. For example, in every cross the parents differ in their mating type, which is controlled by two different alleles, *A* and *a*, at the same locus. Every zygote is, therefore, heterozygous (*Aa*) at this locus, and every ascus contains four ascospores of type *A* and four of type *a*. This is equally true for any other gene for which the parents differ. By following the segregation of the mating types and other introduced gene differences, it has been shown that the chromosomally borne genes are behaving quite normally in asci in which the *mi* and SG variants are showing

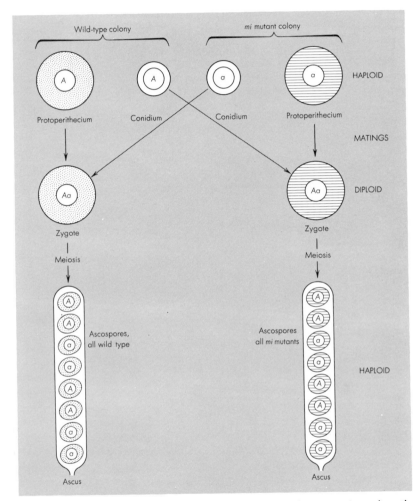

Fig. 4.3. Inheritance of the *mi* mutants of *Neurospora*. When the mutant is used as the female (protoperithecial) parent, all the progeny are mutant; when wild type is used as the female parent, all the progeny are wild type. In both cases, the segregation is 1:1 for each chromosomal gene difference (A,a) in every ascus. Based on Mary B. Mitchell and Herschel K. Mitchell, "A Case of Maternal Inheritance in *Neurospora crassa*," *Proc. Nat. Acad. Sci. U.S.*, 38 (1952).

maternal inheritance. Since, therefore, there is no indication of abnormal chromosomal inheritance, it may be concluded that the *mi* and SG variants of *N. crassa* are controlled by plasmagenes that are almost exclusively maternal in their transmission.

Uniparental transmission in *Chlamydomonas*

Uniparental transfer of extrachromosomal hereditary material does not always have its basis in a visibly unequal parental contribution to the progeny. This is shown by Ruth Sager's investigations of differences between reciprocal crosses in the unicellular green alga *Chlamydomonas reinhardi* (Fig. 4.4). The haploid uninucleate vegeta-

Fig. 4.4. Inheritance of resistance to streptomycin (S^r 500). The plus and minus signs refer to mating type, which is inherited as a single gene difference. The progeny is with rare exceptions always like the plus parent in its reaction to streptomycin, but in these crosses the mating type difference segregates 1:1 in every tetrad. Based on Ruth Sager and F. J. Ryan, *Cell Heredity* (John Wiley & Sons, 1961).

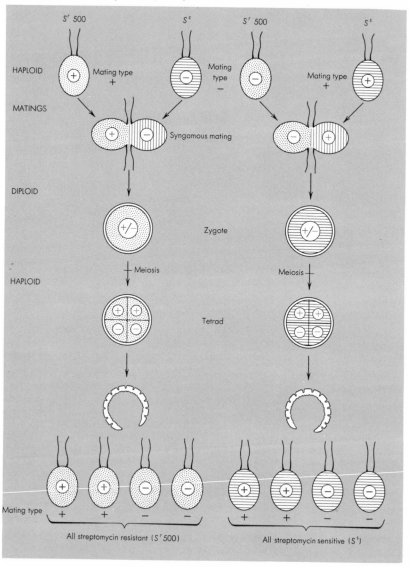

tive cells belong to one of two mating types, mt^+ and mt^-, but the members of these two groups are indistinguishable, except in their ability to mate only with members of the opposite group. Fertilization is syngamous, that is, by complete fusion of two identical individuals of opposite mating type. Each diploid zygote so formed ultimately produces four haploid cells, each of which gives rise to a clone by vegetative multiplication. Two of these are always of mating type mt^+, and two are of mating type mt^-. Indeed, all known chromosomal gene differences in this organism segregate in this way.

In contrast, some mutations to streptomycin resistance and streptomycin dependence do not. For example, one strain is resistant to 500 μ gm. of streptomycin per ml. When crossed reciprocally for mating type with a wild-type sensitive strain, it gives all resistant progeny if the resistant parent is mt^+, and all sensitive progeny if the resistant parent is mt^-, although mutations to resistance can occur in both mating types (Fig. 4.4). Streptomycin dependence of strains that grow better in the presence of 100 μ gm. of streptomycin than in its absence is inherited in exactly the same way. And yet, in the same crosses in which streptomycin resistance and dependence shows uniparental transmission, mating type and other differences controlled by chromosomal gene differences segregate 2:2 in the progeny of each zygote. There can be no doubt, therefore, that the inheritance of streptomycin resistance and dependence is controlled by some extrachromosomal entity that must be present in both parents, and hence must be contributed to the zygote by both parents. But, for some unknown reason, only the contribution of the mt^+ parent is incorporated into the extrachromosomal material of the progeny. There is no obvious physical basis for this uniparental transfer. Hence unequal gametes in the two sexes are not a prerequisite for differences between reciprocal crosses to occur, nor, therefore, do equal gametes ensure equality of the extrachromosomal contribution of the two sexes, or mating types, to the progeny.

Maternal inheritance in *Paramecium*

Persistent differences between reciprocal crosses have only rarely been reported in the animal kingdom, and about half of the known examples occur in a single species, *Paramecium aurelia*. One example of persistent maternal inheritance in this species is described in Chapter 3 (Fig. 3.3), because it illustrates the role of cortical determinants in the inheritance of the external morphology of this organism. Mating type in the B group of varieties and antigen type (serotype) in some stocks of variety 4 of *P. aurelia* show a pattern of inheritance similar to the cortical determinants, but they differ, as we shall see, in one important respect.

The clone of animals produced by each exconjugant obtains its extrachromosomal material primarily from the exconjugant that gave rise to them (see Figs. 3.1 and 3.2.). It is, therefore, uniparental in origin.

If the separation of exconjugants is delayed after mating, there is considerable exchange of the labile extrachromosomal material from one mate to the other. This does not affect the strict maternal inheritance of the cortical determinants (see Fig. 3.3), but it leads to a breakdown in the maternal inheritance of mating type and antigen type. The breakdown has two consequences. First, both exconjugant clones derived from a single mating may have the same phenotype with respect to mating type and antigenic type. Second, one of the exconjugant clones may segregate for the phenotypes of both conjugants. Clearly, the determinants of these two characters, unlike the cortical determinants, reside in the labile extrachromosomal material.

The result of the extrachromosomal exchange between mates differing in their mating type or antigen type is a kind of invasive heredity, which is discussed in greater detail in Chapter 6. At the moment, it is sufficient to note that its occurrence strengthens the argument for the extrachromosomal determination of these characters.

Complex differences

The examples considered in this chapter show simple and usually matroclinous differences between reciprocal crosses. More complex differences between reciprocal crosses are known to result from crossing different varieties or species. In such cases, purely maternal transmission is rare. Sometimes there is a degree of matrocliny, as in the crosses between the two species of moss *Funaria hygrometrica* and *F. mediterranea*. A more typical result, however, is exemplified by extensively analyzed varietal and species crosses in the genus *Epilobium*, where the differences between the reciprocal crosses involve characteristics not present in either parent. Another common situation is for the difference between the reciprocal crosses to emerge for the first time in the F_2, or backcross, generation derived from the initial crosses; the classic instance is male sterility in flax. But in all these and many similar examples, our interest lies not so much in the differences between the reciprocal hybrids as in the interaction between chromosomal genes and maternal extrachromosomal constituents that is revealed in later generations. Details of these examples are given in Chapters 9 and 10, where the whole problem of genome-plasmon relationships is considered.

In conclusion, persistent differences between reciprocal crosses are diagnostic of extrachromosomal heredity if abnormal chromosome behavior, particularly preferential segregation, can be ruled out. Many examples of extrachromosomal heredity in many types of plants and in a few animals are based, at least in part, on this criterion. In most instances the difference between the reciprocal crosses is due to uniparental inheritance, usually maternal or having some degree of matrocliny, as might be expected from the greater extrachromosomal contribution of the maternal parent to the offspring. But this is not always so; a difference between reciprocal crosses may result from the appearance of novel phenotypes in the F_1 or later generations that are not present in either the maternal or the paternal strains. Furthermore, reciprocal differences may arise where the two parents apparently contribute equal amounts of extrachromosomal material to the progeny. This suggests more a basic mechanism for the uniparental transmission of extrachromosomal material than a difference in the sizes of uniting gametes. This point is discussed further in Chapter 7.

References

Caspari, Ernest, "Cytoplasmic Inheritance," *Advan. Genet.*, 2 (1948), 1.

Sager, Ruth, and Y. Tsubo, "Genetic Analysis of Streptomycin Resistance and Dependence in *Chlamydomonas*," *Z. Vererbungslehre, 92* (1961), 430.

Questions

4.1. Why is it necessary to insist that maternal inheritance is persistent before accepting it as evidence for extrachromosomal inheritance?

4.2. Why does the uniparental inheritance of streptomycin resistance and dependence in *Chlamydomonas* show that an inequality in the quantity of extrachromosomal material of uniting gametes is not a prerequisite for maternal inheritance?

Five

Non-Mendelian Segregations

The characteristic segregations of Mendelian genetics are a direct consequence of their genetic determinants being borne on the chromosomes. It might be expected on a priori grounds, therefore, that non-Mendelian segregations would be indicative of hereditary determinants that are not borne on the chromosomes. Indeed, it seems highly improbable that determinants that were not borne on the chromosomes and hence not subject to the strict rules of chromosome behavior could mimic Mendelian segregations. But non-Mendelian segregations can be produced by determinants that have firmly established chromosomal bases. These include such phenomena as gene conversion, paramutation, aneuploidy, and mitotic recombination. Their occurrence must introduce reservations into the use of non-Mendelian segregations as a criterion of extrachromosomal heredity, and it is necessary to bear them in mind in assessing the usefulness of non-Mendelian segregations for detecting extrachromosomal heredity.

Stable segregations

The use of non-Mendelian segregations in the detection of extrachromosomal heredity can be illustrated by reference to a few typical examples.

48

Nonsegregation of mutant phenotypes

We shall start with the class of variant that, when crossed to wild type, never reappears again in the progeny of any generation that may be derived from the initial cross. Typical of this class is the neutral petite variant of yeast (Fig. 5.1), described by Boris Ephrussi and his colleagues. This variant, some of whose properties are described in Chapter 3, is self-sterile. If, however, haploid vegetative cells of the variant are mated to haploid vegetative cells of a normal strain of the opposite mating type, the cells fuse to give diploid vegeta-

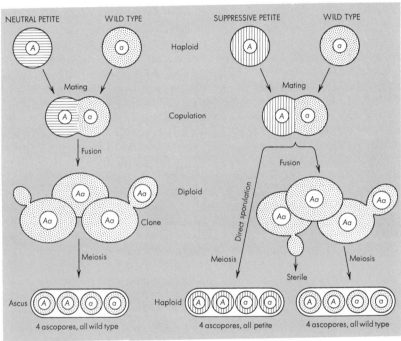

Fig. 5.1. The inheritance of neutral and suppressive petite in yeast. In crosses of wild type to neutral petite, all the progeny are wild type. In crosses of wild type to suppressive petite, the outcome depends on the time of sporulation. If the zygotes are sporulated immediately, most or all the progeny are petite; if they are allowed to grow vegetatively before sporulation, most or all the progeny are wild type. In all cases the chromosomal genes—for example, the mating type genes A and a—segregate 1:1 in every ascus. Based on Boris Ephrussi, Helene Hottinguer, and Herschel Roman, "Suppressiveness: A New Factor in the Genetic Determination of the Synthesis of Respiratory Enzymes in Yeast," *Proc. Nat. Acad. Sci. U.S., 41* (1955).

tive cells that have a normal phenotype and are quite fertile. These diploid cells will multiply indefinitely by a budding process, but under suitable environmental conditions they reproduce sexually, each diploid cell producing an ascus containing four haploid ascospores. These ascospores, whose chromosome complements are the meiotic products of the diploid hybrid, germinate to give rise to clones of haploid vegetative cells. Any gene difference between the parental strains segregates in 1:1 frequencies among the four spores in each ascus. And, of course, this is true for mating type in this particular cross. No petite variants, however, appear in the progeny; all the ascospores produce clones of normal cells. These normal cells were crossed again to the petite variant, and the whole cycle repeated four more times on the progeny of these crosses. At the end of this process, the chromosomal complement of the progeny must have been almost identical with that of the petite strain, but all the progeny were still normal. Occasionally, a petite clone was recovered among these progenies, but with a frequency that was no more than the spontaneous mutation rate from normal to petite.

I have reported a similar situation in *Aspergillus nidulans*. In this normally fertile ascomycete, nonsexual variants are quite common. Through the intermediacy of heterokaryosis with a sexually fertile strain, however, the nonsexual variants may be outcrossed and selfed (self-fertilized). The heterokaryotic state may arise wherever vegetative hyphae of two different homokaryotic strains come into contact (Fig. 5.2). Anastomoses then initiate hyphae that contain the chromosomal and extrachromosomal material of both. In general, however, there is no nuclear fusion in the vegetative cells, hence the different chromosomal complements remain separate and divide mitotically to produce heterokaryotic colonies in which many of the cells contain the chromosomal complements of both homokaryotic components. In *Aspergillus*, a change to a dikaryotic condition, in which the cells contain two nuclei, is the first step in sexual reproduction.

In a heterokaryon, three types of dikaryon may arise: two in which both nuclei are contributed by the same homokaryotic component, and one in which both homokaryotic components contribute a single nucleus. In the majority of cases, one initial dikaryotic cell gives rise to all the dikaryotic cells enclosed within a single perithecium. Hence the three types of dikaryon automatically lead to three types of perithecia. The diploid zygotic nuclei are formed by the fusion of the two haploid chromosome complements in some of the dikaryotic cells. An immediate meiotic division followed by mitosis provides the haploid chromosome complements of the eight ascospores produced by each zygote. Only in those perithecia in which the dikaryon contains one chromosome set from each homokaryon is there any segregation of the genes for which the latter differ, and in these perithecia there is the usual 1 : 1 segregation in every ascus. In the other two types of perithecia, the chromosome complements of the ascospores are uniformly like those of one or the other of the two homokaryotic parents. They are in fact essentially the selfed progeny of the homokaryons.

Heterokaryons between a homokaryotic nonsexual and a homokaryotic sexually fertile strain are fertile and produce three types of perithecia. To ensure easy recognition of the three types, single gene differences may be introduced between the homokaryons. For example, I used a yellow asexually spored variant of the fertile homokaryon—yellow (*y*) is a single gene mutation. Thus a perithecium produced by the heterokaryon, whose contents give only normal green-spored colonies or only yellow-spored colonies must have arisen by the selfing of the green-spored and the yellow-spored components of the heterokaryon, respectively. On the other hand, a perithecium whose contents segregate to give green-spored and yellow-spored colonies in equal numbers can only have arisen from a cross between the two components. With a number of independent nonsexual variants, the contents of all three types of perithecia gave only sexually fertile

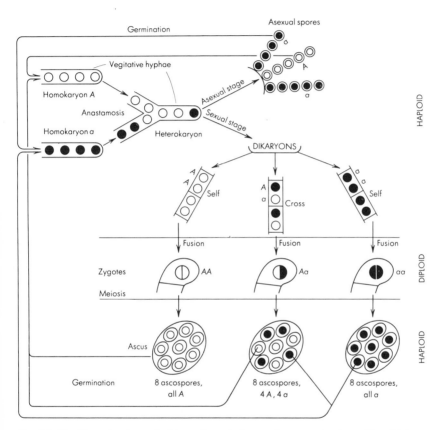

Fig. 5.2. The life cycle of a typical heterokaryotic fungus—for example, *Aspergillus nidulans.* The outcome of asexual and sexual reproduction in a heterokaryon is shown for a single gene difference, A,a. Based on Guido Pontecorvo, "The Genetics of *Aspergillus nidulans*," *Advan. Genet.,* 5 (1953).

colonies, irrespective of their spore color. Thus the nonsexual phenotype did not segregate along with the known gene-controlled differences in the progeny taken from crossed perithecia. Nor did it segregate among the progeny of perithecia, which, judging from the color of their spores, were derived from selfing the nonsexual component of the heterokaryon. These sexually fertile colonies, with the spore color of the original nonsexual strains, were indistinguishable from colonies of the fertile strains for every aspect of their breeding behavior.

Modified barrage phenomenon

An illuminating example in this class is the inheritance of barrage in the ascomycete *Podospora anserina*, whose life cycle is like that of *Neurospora* in all its essential details. Georges Rizet showed that strains of this fungus may be divided into two classes, S and s, on the following test. If an S *strain* is confronted by an s strain, a barrage is produced between them because of a mutual inhibition, but no barrage forms between two S or two s strains. Reciprocal crosses may be made in this fungus as in *Neurospora,* and in reciprocal crosses of S and s strains the s type never appears in either progeny. Instead, a 1:1 segregation is observed in each cross of S, and in a modified s, called s^s, which now forms no barrage with S or s strains. They are, therefore, neither S nor s in their behavior. In the same crosses in which these remarkable changes occur, other genetic differences show strict Mendelian inheritance in every ascus. The nature of the modified reaction of the s strains recovered from the crosses is partially answered by their subsequent breeding behavior. Thus in reciprocal crosses between s and s^s strains, the difference shows strict maternal determination. Since this maternal effect is persistent and is accompanied by no abnormal segregations of known chromosomal genes, it satisfies our first criterion of extrachromosomal heredity (see Chapter 4). Hence the modification of s that leads to non-Mendelian behavior is presumably extrachromosomal in origin.

The three examples just given are all in ascomycete fungi, in which a characteristic of one parent strain never appears in the progeny of an outcross to another strain with a contrasting phenotype. Since the known chromosomal genes of both parental strains were recovered from the progeny in the expected proportions, there is no possibility that one parent did not participate in the cross. Hence the hereditary determinant of the lost parental characteristic must have been permanently changed. That is, the determinant has been modified, replaced, or its action altered. Furthermore, this modification, whatever its nature, occurs with 100 per cent efficiency. Only paramutation among the novel chromosomal causes of non-Mendelian behavior produces changes with a comparable frequency. But paramutation, at least as it is known in maize, is not a satisfactory explanation of the results obtained with neutral petite, nonsexual, and barrage. Its deficiencies may be illustrated as follows. In a cross between two strains, one of which carries a paramutagenic allele and the other a paramutable allele, the latter is modified more or less permanently. This exactly parallels the observed behavior of the three fungal examples. Now if the progeny of this cross were repeatedly backcrossed to the paramutable parent, half the zygotes of the first backcross and a correspondingly greater proportion in subsequent backcrosses would contain a paramutable allele and a paramutated allele. Since the known paramutated alleles have only slight or no paramutagenicity, in the first backcross individuals with the phenotype of the paramutable strain would reappear and their frequency would gradually increase with every additional backcross. This is quite contrary to the result obtained, for example, by repeatedly backcrossing the progeny of a cross between wild-type and neutral petite to the latter strain. Furthermore, the progenies of reciprocal crosses between a strain carrying a paramutated allele and one carrying a paramutable allele are identical. In contrast, the progenies of reciprocal crosses between a modified s strain (s^s) and the original s strain differ because of persistent maternal inheritance. Thus on these two breeding tests alone, paramutation fails as a general explanation of this particular class of non-Mendelian behavior.

Irregular segregations

In the second class of non-Mendelian segregation that we shall consider, the phenotypes of the parental strains reappear in their progeny, but in irregular, non-Mendelian proportions. The suppressive type of petite, described by Boris Ephrussi, Helene Hottinguer, and Herschel Roman, provides a typical instance (Fig. 5.1). Although phenotypically similar, it differs from neutral petite in that it segregates in the progeny of an outcross to a wild-type strain. The difference, however, shows up at an earlier stage. The diploid cells produced by mating haploid cells of a suppressive petite strain with haploid cells of a normal strain of the opposite mating type are of two kinds, giving rise to petite and normal clones respectively. The diploid cells of the petite clones are as sterile as the petite strain itself, while those of the normal clones are fertile. Hence only the latter sporulate and all four ascospores in every ascus that they produce give rise to clones of normal haploid cells. By transferring the diploid cells immediately after they are formed to a medium that promotes sporulation, they all sporulate irrespective of their phenotype. The majority of the ascospores produced now give rise to clones of petite cells, and among the asci produced are found some in which none, one, two, three, or even all four ascospores give rise to clones of petite cells.

The normal and petite strains used in the crosses differed by four genes in addition to mating type. Their segregation was the expected 2:2 in every ascus analyzed. The actual percentage of zygotes that give rise to petite clones varied from nearly zero to nearly 100 per cent, according to the strain of suppressive petite used. It also varied from one occasion to another in crosses using the same petite strain. Thus the suppressive petites not only show non-Mendelian segregations, but all kinds of extraneous circumstances, which have no effect on chromosomal gene segregations, alter their segregation pattern.

Similar examples are known in two species of *Aspergillus*. In *A. glaucus,* whose life cycle is the same at that of *A. nidulans* in all essential details (Fig. 5.2), H. Subak Sharpe has described a conidial variant that, when crossed to wild type via the intermediary of heterokaryosis, showed irregular segregation. These irregularities were of two kinds. First, the conidial and normal phenotypes segregated in irregular proportions in all three types of perithecium produced by the heterokaryon. Thus even in the progeny of the selfed perithecia there was a segregation of this difference. Second, while all the known gene differences between the conidial and the normal homokaryons segregated 1:1 in the individual asci from the mixed perithecia, the segregation into conidial and normal phenotypes occurred in all possible proportions. Virtually identical results have been obtained by Morris Grindle in crosses between the so-called purple variant and normal homokaryons of *A. nidulans*.

Although a number of chromosomally based systems can produce irregular segregations, two of these systems, gene conversion and mitotic recombination, do not produce the range or frequency of irregularities recorded for suppressive petite, conidial, and purple. Also, it is unlikely that mitotic recombination could lead to the irregular segregations without producing similar irregularities for the known gene-controlled differences that were segregating in the same crosses. If the variants were aneuploids, however, they might well show irregular segregations with as much variety and with the frequency observed when outcrossed to a strain with a normal chromosome complement. Indeed, they might even show such segregations on selfing, as do the self-fertile conidial and purple variants. On the other hand, aneuploidy cannot explain the segregation observed in the selfed progeny of a normal strain produced while in heterokaryotic association with the conidial or purple variant. Nor, in fact, can any of the other known chromosomal causes of non-Mendelian segregation. Since the aberrant segregations of suppressive petite, conidial, and purple are not readily explicable in terms of any of the known kinds of chromosomal behavior, they are acceptable as evidence of an extrachromosomal basis.

Somatic segregations

Mendelian segregation of genes is the direct consequence of the meiotic behavior of the chromosomes on which they are borne. The absence of segregation of genes in somatic cells during those periods of the life cycle in which all cell reproduction is vegetative or asexual is similarly a result of the mitotic division of the chromosomes in the multiplication of these cells. In general, therefore, segregation among somatic cells at vegetative or asexual reproduction is not likely to result from the segregation of chromosomal genes. Hence its occurrence could be indicative of the segregation of extrachromosomally borne plasmagenes. There are, however, other causes of somatic segregation that require consideration.

If a viable gene or chromosomal mutation occurs in one haploid uninucleate organism of a clone, all members of which are reproducing vegetatively, there is an immediate intraclonal segregation. A similar mutation in one haploid nucleus of the multinucleate growing tips of a fungal colony would not lead to an immediate segregation. It would, however, initiate a heterokaryotic growing point that could subsequently lead to an intraclonal segregation. Thus the continued mitotic division of the mutant nucleus could in time produce a growing tip that contained only mutant nuclei and, if the latter could compete in growth with the neighboring tips containing normal nuclei, a segregation could result with the production of sectors with the mutant phenotype. Furthermore, if the colony produced asexual spores, some would contain normal and others mutant nuclei; if the spores were multinucleate, some might contain both. Hence propagation of the colony by asexual spores could lead to a segregation into normal and mutant homokaryons and, if some of the asexual spores contain both normal and mutant nuclei, some of the segregants would be heterokaryotic. In higher plants, a dominant mutation in the chromosome complement of one of the diploid meristematic cells would be required to produce somatic segregation, and the result would be a sectoring chimaera. Animal chimaeras could also result from similar mutations in the chromosome complement of actively dividing cells.

Such mutations are rare events, and once the segregation they lead to has occurred it is not usually repeated until there is another similar rare mutation. Mutable loci are known at which there are frequent mutations, with a resulting persistent somatic segregation. In such cases, however, the segregation is unidirectional because the high mutability extends to the forward but not to the backward direction of mutation; that is, a phenotype A is continually sectoring to give phenotype B, but the B phenotype is, relatively speaking, quite stable. A similar high frequency of unidirectional segregation would be produced by a mitotically unstable aneuploid in which the chromosomes in excess of the normal complement were continually being lost. Again, once these were lost, the chromosome complement would become stable, and hence incapable of producing further segregation by changes in the complement.

A further source of somatic segregation, namely, mitotic recombination, is also a rare occurrence wherever heterozygous diploid chromosome complements are dividing mitotically. The heterozygous diploid condition is commonplace in all higher organisms, but it also occurs with a very low frequency in organisms with haploid vegetative stages, for example, where different haploid nuclei, brought together in heterokaryotic or dikaryotic association, fuse to produce heterozygous diploids. More than one process is probably involved in the somatic segregation of the heterozygous diploids. The consequence of these processes, which is all that concerns us here, is that chromosome complements arise that are homozygous. These homozygous combinations may be identical with the parental homozygotes or they may involve reassortments or recombinations of the parental complements. In organisms that are normally haploid an additional process, namely, haploidization, occurs. This involves a reduction of the diploid complement to its former haploid state. During haploidization many intermediate aneuploids are produced that are mitotically unstable, and hence add to the segregations that occur. Mitotic recombination is widespread in its occurrence, having been observed in organisms as diverse as the fruit fly, *Drosophila*, and fungi. Its frequency, however, even under optimal experimental conditions, is of the order of spontaneous gene mutation.

Since there is a variety of rare chromosomal mechanisms that can lead to somatic segregation, we cannot automatically refer somatic segregation to extrachromosomal agencies. On the other hand, a regular, persistent somatic segregation seems to be characteristic of certain extrachromosomal variants and this property may, therefore, be used as a criterion for their detection.

Plastid segregations

Foremost among the examples of somatic segregation are the plastid variegations of higher plants, which have been discussed in a different connection in Chapters 3 and 4. The sectoring is not in itself indicative of extrachromosomal inheritance, for, as we saw, the subsequent inheritance of the abnormal plastid phenotype could be Mendelian or extrachromosomal. Sectors arise, therefore, by gene or plasmagene mutation. For some of the extrachromosomally inherited variegations, cells with mixed plastids have been observed. In these cases, the pattern of segregation into sectors containing only normal and only abnormal plastids is consistent with the sorting out of the plastids of the mixed cells during their mitotic multiplication. (See Chapters 3, 4, and 8.) Even where, as in maize, cells with mixed plastids have not been observed, plants with extrachromosomally inherited variegations may produce three classes of offspring, normal green, mutant yellow, and variegated plants with sectors. Since these plastid variegations show strict maternal determination, the three classes of offspring must imply three classes of female gametes. Hence the extrachromosomal determinants of a variegated plant must be contained in its maternal gamete, and the sectors must arise by their mitotic segregation during the development of the plant. Where all three classes of offspring are produced from seed on a single ear of maize, their distribution on the ear is not random. Thus a sector of an ear that yields the variegated seedlings is usually situated between sectors that produce only green and only yellow seedlings. Again, this suggests somatic segregation of the extrachromosomal determinant during the development of the ear.

Somatic segregation undoubtedly occurs in *Nepeta cataria* and in *Oenothera*, where sectors appear in the progeny of certain crosses due to the somatic segregation of different plastids contributed to the zygote by the male and female parents. On the whole, therefore, there is ample evidence that the plasmagenes or plastogenes that control the phenotype of the plastids segregate during mitotic cell divisions.

Somatically unstable variants of Aspergillus

The plastid variegations provide a useful model for the interpretation of persistent somatic segregations in the fungi. The latter have the advantage that single vegetative hyphae and asexually produced spores will initiate colonies, and hence a segregation can be followed over an indefinite number of somatic cell generations without the intervention of sexual reproduction. The most fully investigated examples are found in the fungus *Aspergillus nidulans,* where they have been extensively examined by me and by C. F. Arlett and Morris Grindle. Colonies of this species, as we have seen (Fig. 5.2), produce haploid uninucleate asexual spores and haploid uninucleate sexual spores. If, therefore, a colony is initiated by germinating a single spore, we would expect all the nuclei of its vegetative cells and spores to be identical. Nevertheless, over twenty independent variants of this fungus, some spontaneous, others induced, segregate and sector repeatedly among the vegetative hyphae and spores produced by a colony that has been initiated by a single spore. In some instances, the segregation and sectoring is into two phenotypically distinct types; in others, the segregation is continuous, for no major classes are recognizable, although the extreme phenotypes often differ for many important properties. The variants that segregate into two classes have the common property that one of the segregant classes has the phenotype of the normal strain from which the variant originated, and the other segregant is the variant itself. A variant colony, whether initiated by a single asexual spore or a single vegetative hypha, invariably segregates, and transfers of such a colony, either by asexual spores or vegetative hyphae, produce two classes of colony, normal and variant. While the colonies that are initially variant in phenotype always segregate, the behavior of those with a normal phenotype varies.

This behavior can be illustrated by a specific example, namely, the "red" variant (Fig. 5.3). Some of the colonies obtained from the asexual spores of a red variant have normal phenotypes, while others have red phenotypes. The asexual spores of the latter repeat this segregation on germination, giving from 10 to 90 per cent colonies with red phenotypes. The asexual spores of the normal segregants, on the other hand, germinate to give at least 90 per cent normal colonies and less than 10 per cent variant colonies. Transfers of vegetative cells from the two kinds of colony behave in much the same way as the asexual spores. The minute variant is similar. It differs from red in that the normal segregants never segregate again; they always breed true. To give some idea of the persistency of the segregation, the first colony with the so-called red phenotype was obtained in 1955. Since that time, it has been propagated at approximately two weekly intervals by vegetative hyphae and asexual spores. When transferring by asexual spores, a colony with a red phenotype was always chosen as the source of asexual spores for the next transfer. Hence some cultures of the present-day red variant have passed through more than two hundred successive propagations by single uninucleate haploid spores. Yet these cultures still segregate, as indeed they have in every one of the approximately ten thousand asexual progenies taken from them.

The segregation of the red, minute, and similar variants is into two classes that can be unambiguously classified on the basis of their colonial appearance. With respect to other characteristics, the segregation is continuous. As examples, the segregants with a red phenotype grow 27 per cent faster on average and have 49 per cent fewer perithecia than the normal segregants. There is nevertheless an overlap for these two properties between segregants with red and normal phenotypes. Similarly, normal colonies always give fewer red segregants in their asexual progenies than do colonies with a red phenotype (Fig. 5.3). But there is in fact a continuous distribution of proportions

Fig. 5.3. Typical lineage of a persistently segregating variant, the red variant of *Aspergillus nidulans*. Every colony in the lineage is initiated from a single uninucleate haploid spore. The asexual spores produced by the colonies with a variant phenotype germinate to give colonies that segregate into normal and variant phenotypes. The colonies with the variant phenotypes invariably repeat this segregation; those with a normal phenotype sometimes breed true.

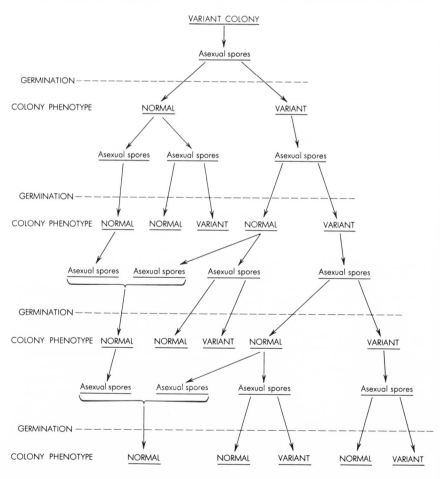

of red segregants in the asexual progenies of normal and red parent colonies that ranges from zero to 95 per cent. All three characters agree in indicating a continuous variation, and indeed these three characters are highly correlated in their variation. It appears, therefore, that the discontinuity in colonial morphology must result from a threshold effect in an underlying, continuously varying system.

It must be apparent from the properties of persistent segregations in fungi that they cannot be satisfactorily explained by any of the known genic or chromosomal causes of somatic segregation. They fail primarily because the segregation that would result from a highly mutable chromosomal gene or an unstable aneuploidy would be unidirectional, while the examples described often are not. To give an illustration, not only do the colonies with a red phenotype give some normal segregants in their asexual progeny, but the normal segregants give some red segregants in their own asexual progenies. Since each colony is initiated from a single uninucleate haploid spore, any genic or chromosomal change that could explain the former segregation must be reversible with a similar frequency to explain the latter segregation. Neither the high mutation rate of a mutable gene nor the loss of the excess chromosomes of an aneuploid are reversible with a frequency that is comparable with the forward event. Furthermore, since the frequency of gene mutation in the variant strains, combined with cytological observations and breeding tests, confirm the uninucleate haploid condition of the asexual spores, an explanation based on aneuploidy or mitotic recombination in a heterozygous diploid starts off at a serious disadvantage.

Not all instances of persistent segregation are confined to *Aspergillus nidulans*. They have been described in *A. glaucus*, various *Penicillium* species, and in *Nectria stenospora*, and there is no morphological or physiological property of a fungal colony that has not shown segregation in one or another of these examples. Indeed, there is every indication that persistent segregations of the type described in *A. nidulans* are as commonplace among fungi as are plastid variegations in higher plants.

Somatic recombination

A further criterion of extrachromosomal heredity depends on the properties of mitotically dividing chromosomal complements, namely, that if different nuclei are associated in the same somatic cell in which all divisions are mitotic, they maintain their integrity because no exchange of chromosomal hereditary material occurs. The conditions under which this test can be carried out are restricted by the requirement of bringing two different chromosomal complements together by cell conjunction under conditions where fusion of the different complements does not occur, so that the different complements, or their mitotic products, may be re-extracted after a period of coexistence in the same cell. In the heterokaryotic fungi and in the dikaryotic stage of some basidiomycetes, this sequence of events occurs naturally when two compatible homokaryons or monokaryons meet (Fig. 5.2). In other fungi the sequence may be initiated artificially or terminated by micrurgical techniques. Outside the fungi, however, this test is at the moment impossible for technical reasons.

In the heterokaryotic and dikaryotic states, the haploid chromosomal complements of different strains and the mitotic products of these complements may coexist indefinitely within the same cell membrane. Where the heterokaryon or dikaryon produces uninucleate asexual spores, or spores containing only the mitotic products of a single nucleus, it is automatically resolved into its two component strains, and by germinating the spores the two components may be recovered (Fig. 5.2). As far as their genomes are concerned, the re-extracted strains should be identical with those of the original strains; indeed, the former are the direct mitotic products of the latter. Hence for all gene-controlled characteristics, the phenotypes of the original and re-extracted strains should be identical. This expectation has been exhaustively confirmed in many species of fungi, using known gene differences. But rare exceptions are known; among them the most important is mitotic recombination, some of whose properties have already been mentioned. The heterokaryotic and dikaryotic conditions provide an opportunity for heterozygous diploid chromosomal complements to arise in somatic cells, and it is known that they do so with a frequency of about 10^{-6}. The heterozygous diploid then provides an opportunity for genic combinations to arise that differ from those of the original strains. Thus it destroys the integrity of the different genomes associated in a heterokaryon or a dikaryon. A further possibility that must be considered is that genomes associated in the same cell but not in the same nucleus could permanently affect one another by a process akin to paramutation. There is, of course, no evidence that paramutation can operate across the extrachromosomal barrier that separates different chromosome sets in a heterokaryon or dikaryon, as it does between homologous loci in the same chromosome complement of a heterozygous diploid. Nevertheless, it must be borne in mind as a possible interpretation in cases in which one component of such an association is permanently changed by its partner.

Heterokaryon test

The outcome of this test, often called "the heterokaryon test," can be illustrated by reference to variants of the *Aspergilli*, which have already given indications of extrachromosomal inheritance with respect to earlier criteria. The simplest example is provided by the nonsexual strains of *A. nidulans*, which, it may be recalled, show non-Mendelian segregations when crossed to normal, sexually fertile strains. As a preliminary to crossing in this species, a heterokaryon must be made between the nonsexual and normal strain. If the latter carries the *y* allele, which gives yellow as opposed to green *Y* asexual spores, the heterokaryon produces both green and yellow asexual spores, their genomes being derived from the nonsexual and normal strains respectively. On germination, therefore, each spore gives a homokaryotic colony with either all green or all yellow asexual spores, but every colony so obtained, whether green- or yellow-spored, is sexually fertile. Clearly, the phenotype of the nonsexual strain has been permanently changed by its coexistence in the same vegetative cells with the normal strain.

In other examples, it is the normal strain whose phenotype is permanently affected by its variant partner. Such an example is provided by the "vegetative death" variant of *A. glaucus*. The characteristic appearance of colonies of this variant is due to the frequent death, accompanied by swelling and lysis, of the hyphae, the low production of asexual spores, and the absence of any sexual stage. The heterokaryon between vegetative death and a normal strain carrying a number of mutant alleles affecting spore color and colonial morphology sooner or later shows the characteristic phenotype of vegetative death. Because some of the asexual spores of *A. glaucus* strains are multinucleate, the heterokaryon produces some heterokaryotic spores in addition to the two kinds of homokaryon. After germination, however, all three types are unambiguously classifiable by reference to the gene-controlled differences in asexual spore color and colonial morphology. All three types are, in fact, recovered from heterokaryons between vegetative death and normal strains, and all show the symptoms of vegetative death to the same extent.

While the results obtained with nonsexual and vegetative death are typical of many, the outcome of the heterokaryon test is, in general, somewhat more complex. One frequent cause of complication is the persistent segregation of the variant. From heterokaryons between the persistently segregating purple variant of *A. nidulans* and a normal strain carrying a number of major gene-markers, asexual spores are obtained that give four classes on germination (Fig. 5.4). First, the colonies obtained from the asexual spores can be divided into two classes, those possessing the combination of alleles present in the original variant strain, and those possessing the alternative combination of alleles present in the original normal strain. Second, each of these classes can be subdivided into two others, those having the variant phenotype and showing persistent segregation for the purple-nonpurple difference, and those having the nonpurple phenotype and breeding true. It appears, therefore, that there has been a reciprocal reassortment between the known chromosomal gene-markers and the determinants of the purple-nonpurple differences, to give four combinations in all, while the strains were associated in the heterokaryotic state. One of the apparent reassortments, the class with the combination of alleles of the variant, but with the nonpurple phenotype, is continually arising by the persistent segregation of the purple variant without the intervention of heterokaryosis. Hence only one class, the colonies with the combination of alleles of the normal strain, but with the purple phenotype, is a novel combination that could only have arisen from the heterokaryotic association. The existence of this class, which constitutes some 20 per cent of the colonies produced by the asexual spores of the heterokaryon, is the evidence for somatic reassortment. Similar results have been obtained with the persistently segregating red variant. This variant has been successfully reassorted with the genomes of six strains through the intermediary of heterokaryosis.

In all, some fifteen independent variants in seven species of ascomycetes have shown somatic reassortment with a contrasting phenotype in a heterokaryon test. These include most of the persistently segregating variants of *A. nidulans* and *A. glaucus* that show continuous and discontinuous variation, the *mi* variants of *Neurospora crassa*, and the petite variants of the yeast *Saccharomyces cereviseae*.

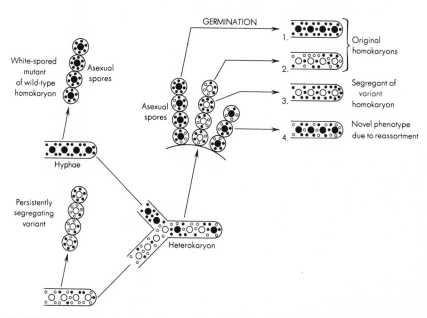

Fig. 5.4. The outcome of a heterokaryon test between a persistently segregating variant—for example, the red or purple variant of *Aspergillus nidulans*—and a wild-type strain. Four homokaryons are obtained on germinating the asexual spores produced by the heterokaryon. One of these four could have arisen only by reassortment of extrachromosomal determinants in the heterokaryon. The chromosomal gene differences between the homokaryons behave as expected (see Fig. 5.2). Based on C. F. Arlett, Morris Grindle, and John L. Jinks, "The Red Cytoplasmic Variant of *Aspergillus nidulans*," *Heredity*, 17 (1962).

A most interesting application of the heterokaryon test on *S. cereviseae* (Fig. 5.5) has been described by R. E. Wright and Joshua Lederberg. Normally, when two haploid yeast cells conjugate, nuclear fusion occurs immediately and the first vegetative cell budded from the conjugated cells is diploid. Strains are known, however, where diploidization is delayed, so that the product of cell conjugation is a heterokaryon containing different haploid chromosome complements. The heterokaryon is resolved into its components once more by the production of haploid buds containing the chromosome complement of one or the other of the original strains. It is possible, therefore, temporarily to associate normal and petite strains in this way and to re-extract haploid cells with the genome of one or the other strain. Some

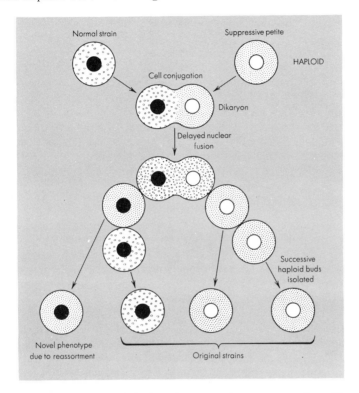

Fig. 5.5. The outcome of the heterokaryon test between suppressive petite and a wild-type strain. In the strains used, the nuclear fusion that normally follows immediately upon cell conjugation is delayed, so that the buds produced by the conjugants are haploid and identical in the genes they carry with one or other of the parent strains. Some of these buds have a novel phenotype, possessing the gene-controlled characteristics of the wild-type strain and the phenotype and breeding behavior of suppressive petite. These could have arisen only by the reassortment of extrachromosomal determinants. Based on R. E. Wright and Joshua Lederberg, "Extranuclear Transmission in Yeast Heterokaryons," *Proc. Nat. Acad. Sci. U.S.*, 43 (1957).

of these haploid cells possess the genome of the normal partner, but permanently display the properties and breeding behavior of a petite mutant.

In each heterokaryon test, at least one known chromosomal gene difference distinguishes the homokaryotic (or monokaryotic) components. This provides an internal check that chromosomal behavior is normal. Where, as in the majority of tests, the components differ at many gene loci, they also provide a check that mitotic recombination of chromosomal genes is not occurring; if it were occurring, these genes would appear in novel combinations in the asexual progeny of the heterokaryon. We can be fairly confident, therefore, that the claims of extrachromosomal inheritance based on the heterokaryon test cannot be referred to either abnormal chromosomal behavior or mitotic recombination. This leaves only paramutation as a possible genic explanation of the results. Given that paramutagenesis can occur between alleles carried in different chromosomal complements separated by extrachromosomal material, paramutation might explain the conversion of the nonsexual strains to sexual fertility, or the normal strains to vegetative death. It is not easy to see how it could possibly explain more. Thus in most cases the heterokaryon test provides results that are not explicable on the basis of any known kind of chromosomal heredity. The results are, on the other hand, what one would expect if determinants that are not physically attached to the chromosomes were responsible for the variant phenotypes.

Concluding remarks

Segregation is clearly a characteristic of extrachromosomal heredity. It differs from the meiotic segregation of chromosomal heredity in that it does not obey Mendelian laws and in that it occurs equally at meiotic and mitotic divisions. If the mitotic segregation of extrachromosomally inherited differences occurs in a heterokaryon, it leads to the reassortment or recombination of the extrachromosomally and chromosomally inherited differences that distinguish the components of the heterokaryon. Equally characteristic of extrachromosomal heredity is the regular absence of segregation at meiosis following a cross between two contrasting phenotypes. These properties jointly provide some of the most powerful criteria for the recognition of extrachromosomal heredity. Unfortunately, however, technical considerations virtually confine the use of these tests to the fungi.

References

Ephrussi, Boris, *Nucleo-cytoplasmic Relations in Micro-Organisms.* New York: Oxford University Press, 1953.

Jinks, John L., "Cytoplasmic Inheritance in Fungi," in *Methodology in Basic Genetics*, W. J. Burdette, ed. (San Francisco: Holden-Day, Inc., 1963).

Michaelis, Peter, "Genetische, entwicklungsgeschichtliche, und zytologische Untersuchungen zur Plasmavererbung, I," *Flora (Jena), 151* (1961), 162.

Questions

5.1. How would you attempt to distinguish between chromosomal and extrachromosomal heredity in a self-fertile fungus that will form heterokaryons—for example, *Aspergillus nidulans?* How does your approach differ from that used with a self-sterile fungus—for example, *Neurospora crassa?*

5.2. A heterokaryon was made between a green-spored, diffuse strain of *Aspergillus nidulans* and a strain that produced white spores because of the gene mutation *w*, and compact colonies because of gene mutation *co*. It also produced a purple pigment. One hundred colonies were raised from the asexual spores produced by the heterokaryon. They could be classified into the following four classes: green-spored, diffuse, 49; white-spored, compact, 8; green-spored, diffuse, purple, 22; white-spored, compact, purple, 21. Explain this result.

Changes in the Extrachromosomal
Complement

There are two principal ways in which the extrachromosomal complement of a cell can be changed, by mutation and by infection. Mutation involves a modification in an extrachromosomal components of a cell; infection involves the acquisition of extrachromosomal components from a different plasmon. Many of the conditions under which these changes can be brought about and the frequency with which they often occur have no counterparts at the chromosomal level. Hence an extrachromosomal basis for a change in phenotype can sometimes be inferred from the conditions under which it can be induced.

Specific mutagens and high frequencies of mutation

The predictability of Mendelian inheritance depends as much on the stability of its determinants as it does on the precision of chromosome behavior. Nevertheless, the determinants do change and the extremely low frequency of such changes can be considerably raised by various treatments that are mutagenic. In general, the mutagens are nonspecific, in that they raise the frequency of mutation at all loci, although some may raise the frequency at one locus somewhat more than at another. Even with the most efficient mutagen, only the minority of the survivors of the treatment will have mutated.

Many variants, for which there is evidence of extra-chromosomal inheritance, have been induced by external treatments. The high mutation rates and the specificity of the mutagen in many of these inductions have no counterparts in chromosomal gene mutations, and hence they prospectively provide additional evidence of an extrachromosomal basis. The classic example of specific induction is the production of petite variants of yeast by acridine dyes, such as euflavine and acriflavine. The petite variant arises spontaneously with a low frequency, and in almost any sample of yeast cells approximately 1 per cent will be found to give rise to petite colonies. Under ideal conditions, yeast cells that have previously grown in the presence of acriflavine (concn. 10^{-6}) will give rise to 100 per cent petite colonies. Furthermore, the treatment always produces the same variant, and it does so without any lethality among the treated cells, and hence without any selection. Another chemical mutagen, tetrazolium chloride, is only slightly less effective in inducing the petite variant.

If single yeast cells are exposed to a concentration of 10^{-6} parts of euflavine and the successive buds are isolated as produced, and washed and transferred to acridine free medium, at least half give rise to petite colonies. But the most interesting aspect of this is that a treated cell that has produced mutant buds is still capable of producing some normal ones, and the treated cell itself is often normal. Thus the mutagen may produce an unstable state in the treated cells, so that they haphazardly produce normal buds and mutant buds in turn.

Acriflavine is now known to be generally effective, at least among the fungi, in producing variants that subsequently show extrachromosomal inheritance. Among these are the minute and mycelial mutants of *Aspergillus nidulans* and the SG and many other variants in *Neurospora crassa*. Details of the treatments are available only for the minute variant, where the mutagen, used at a concentration of 10^{-5}, produces solely minute variants with a high frequency and without any lethality.

Elevated temperatures have also been highly successful in inducing variants that show extrachromosomal transmission. Yields as high as 95 per cent of petite variants have been obtained from yeast cells grown at 40°C. Since petite cells do not grow or divide faster than normal cells under these conditions, this result must be due to mutation rather than to a selective increase in the low frequency of petite cells, which are always present as a result of spontaneous mutation. Selection has also been ruled out as the explanation of the somewhat less specific and less effective result of elevated temperatures on *A. nidulans*. Four persistently segregating variants, which differ from normal in perithecial production and rate of growth, have nevertheless been induced by high temperatures in this species with frequencies around 2 per cent. These variants were not observed in parallel cultures grown at 25°C., although they had markedly abnormal phenotypes at this temperature and hence would have been detected had they arisen.

There is conflicting evidence about the mutagenic activity of anaerobiosis, although there is general agreement that there is no preferential selection of the anaerobic petite cells under these conditions. M. Harris found no induction; C. C. Lindegren and S. Hino found a tenfold increase in the frequency of petite cells under anaerobic conditions. Ultraviolet irradiation, on the other hand, undoubtedly increases the mutation rate to petite. D. D. Pittman observed as many as 23 per cent petites among the cells that survived ultraviolet irradiation, a frequency that was independent of the chromosomal ploidy. Furthermore, there was no differential sensitivity of normal or petite cells to the irradiation, and hence no selective killing. Ultraviolet irradiation also gave rise to the red variant of *A. nidulans* and a compact variant of *A. glaucus*, but with frequencies that do not distinguish them from similarly induced gene mutations.

Extrachromosomally inherited mutations that affect the phenotype of the plastids occur spontaneously in all green plants. In *Oenothera*, approximately 0.02 per cent of plants show the yellow or white cells, or segments characteristic of these mutations, and in *Epilobium* the frequency is around 0.08 per cent. The spontaneous mutation rates may be raised by X-irradiation of seed, or by the incorporation of radioactive isotypes such as S^{35} and P^{32} into the growing plant. For example, Peter Michaelis raised the incidence of such mutations in *Epilobium* to 0.77 per cent by S^{35}. But these induced mutations are not distinguished from chromosomal gene mutations, either in their frequency or in the specificity of the mutagens. Agents that specifically inhibit chlorophyll production and suppress plastid development are known, however, but these appear to have no mutagenic effect in higher organisms. For example, streptomycin has such an effect on seedlings of *Hordeum vulgare*, but while it is irreversible in those cells produced during the treatment, the meristem can generate normal green leaves after the treatment is discontinued. The same treatment, it may be recalled, specifically and with a high frequency permanently rids *Euglena gracilis* of its chloroplasts (see Chapters 2 and 3). The same is also true for many other chemical and physical treatments. Ruth Sager has recently shown that extrachromosomally inherited defects in the photosynthetic system of *Chlamydomonas reinhardi* are induced by streptomycin. These include auxotrophic mutants, which require acetate for growth, and a mutant that cannot synthesize chlorophyll in the dark. This mutagen also induces the extrachromosomally inherited streptomycin-resistant and streptomycin-dependent mutants that are described in Chapter 4. Streptomycin, however, does not induce at a high frequency nor, in view of the variety of mutations it has induced, can its action be specific.

Although not mutagenic treatments in the usual sense, certain methods of stock maintenance lead to a high frequency of a particular variant whose subsequent inheritance is extrachromosomal. Thus aging, achieved by purely vegetative maintenance of *A. glaucus*, leads to degenerative changes that culminate in vegetative death. The duration of aging before the latter occurs may vary from four months to two years, but the incidence, once it occurs, is very high, and independently maintained subcolonies of the same strain are affected almost simultaneously. In this same category belongs the s^s variant of *Podospora anserina*, which is invariably produced whenever an S strain is crossed by an s strain.

These examples serve to demonstrate that some, though not all, extrachromosomally inherited variants may be specifically induced with a high frequency by an appropriate mutagen, and hence that this property is itself indicative of an extrachromosomal basis. Furthermore, a variant that may be so induced has satisfied an unambiguous criterion of extrachromosomal heredity, for no known chromosomal gene possesses comparable properties. On the other hand, the inability to induce specifically a particular variant with a high frequency can in no way detract from any other evidence in favor of an extrachromosomal basis, for there is always the possibility that the appropriate mutagen has yet to be found.

Invasion

At certain stages in the life cycle of some organisms, the nuclear and extranuclear materials are capable of characteristically different degrees of movement. Where this difference is sufficiently pronounced, it can form a basis for distinguishing between hereditary determinants contained within and without the nuclear membrane. For instance, in the filamentous ascomycetes the vegetative hyphae are not divided by true cell walls; instead their internal diameter is constricted at intervals by annular thickenings through which the cytoplasm is continuous. The nuclei are often smaller than the central pore and could, therefore, pass from one "cell" to another. In practice, they rarely seem to do so. Thus if two different homokaryons of *A. nidulans* or *A. glaucus* are grown side by side on the same plate, hyphal anastomosis will produce heterokaryotic cells, and these in turn will produce a heterokaryotic sector that will grow with the homokaryons on either side of it. But there is no invasion of the hyphae of one homokaryon by nuclei from the other, hence there is no wholesale conversion of homokaryotic cells into heterokaryons.

If we now grow a normal homokaryon and a conidial or vegetative death variant of *A. glaucus* side by side in this way, heterokaryon sectors will be formed between them, but between these sectors and the normal homokaryon an ever widening sector will appear that will gradually replace the normal homokaryon (Fig. 6.1). This sector has the conidial or vegetative death phenotype, but otherwise it has all the known gene-controlled characteristics of the normal homokaryon. This modified normal strain is permanently changed and breeds true for its new phenotype, whether propagated by hyphae or spores. The hyphal anastomoses that initiated the heterokaryon have apparently provided a route whereby the determinants of the conidial and vegetative death phenotypes could penetrate the homokaryotic hyphae of

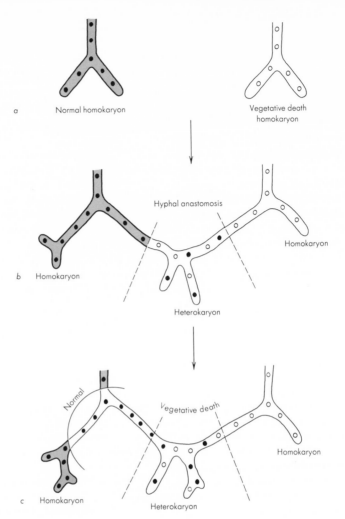

Fig. 6.1. The invasive spread of vegetative death from a strain showing this property to a normal strain of *Aspergillus glaucus*. (*a*) The normal strain has straight, regularly branched hyphae; the vegetative death strain has thinner walled, irregular hyphae with occasional swollen growing tips. (*b*) Invasion occurs only if the contact between hyphae of the normal and mutant strains results in hyphal anastomosis and the production of heterokaryotic hyphae. The heterokaryon soon shows the symptoms of vegetative death. (*c*) Vegetative death is later shown by the homokaryotic hyphae of the normal strain, which are now in cytoplasmic continuity with the mutant strain via the heterokaryon. By sampling the asexual spores and growing tips in the region of contact between the two homokaryons and the heterokaryon, it can be shown that the causal agent of vegetative death spreads into the normal homokaryon far beyond the point of maximum penetration of the nuclei of the vegetative death strain. Based on John L. Jinks, "Lethal, Suppressive Cytoplasms in Aged Clones of *Aspergillus glaucus*," *J. Gen. Microbiol.*, 21 (1959).

the normal strain and, furthermore, penetrate well beyond the maximum point of penetration of the known chromosomally borne determinants. Thus we have achieved an automatic fractionation of the hereditary determinants of the variant homokaryons by their differential mobility or ability to penetrate established homokaryotic hyphae. This ability has been referred to as "infective heredity."

In two instances of infective heredity involving vegetative death and the similar variant of *Podospora anserina* known as senescence, it has been established that anastomosis between the vegetative hyphae of the normal and variant colonies is an essential preliminary to the infective spread of the variant phenotype. Furthermore, neither contact with hyphae of the vegetative death strain without the opportunity for anastomosis nor a cell-free extract of the hyphae of vegetative death or of the medium in which it has grown will produce even a temporary modification of the phenotype of a normal strain. The outcome of the infection is identical with that of a heterokaryon test. A novel phenotype is produced; it is like one homokaryon strain in its known gene-controlled characteristics, but it is also like another, with which it has been in contact or in heterokaryotic association, in characteristics that appear to be extrachromosomally determined.

A gradual invasion of determinants from a donor hypha of a senescent strain to an acceptor hypha of a normal strain has been demonstrated at the microscopic level. Following an observed anastomosis between a single senescent hypha and a single normal hypha, the hyphae produced by the continued growth of the normal hypha were cut off, grown, and their phenotypes observed at various times. Many of these transferred hyphae, all of which had the genotype of the original normal strain, showed characteristics of senescence, but there was a gradient. Hyphae taken from the point nearest the anastomosis showed the most marked senescence. Hyphae taken from farther away showed equally marked senescence only after a correspondingly longer period following the anastomosis. Clearly, some agent that causes senescence was gradually moving from the senescent to the normal hypha through the anastomosis. Since none of the transfers from branches of the normal hypha, when tested, was heterokaryotic, this agent could not have been migrating nuclei. It must, therefore, have been extranuclear.

In conjugating *Paramecium*, it is the nuclear material that is migratory and the extranuclear material that often remains *in situ*. This results in differences between reciprocal exconjugant clones whenever the conjugants differ in their extranuclear hereditary make-up. Thus in *Paramecium*, as in the filamentous ascomycetes, it is the differential mobility of nuclear and extranuclear material that allows their separation in breeding experiments. This situation, which is described in Chapter 4 and in Fig. 6.2, may be modified by different circumstances; in some strains it can be modified by a delay in the separation of the conjugants, so that there is a considerable movement of extranuclear material between them. The consequence is a partial or complete breakdown of the difference between reciprocal exconjugant clones, for each clone becomes invaded by hereditary determinants that are usually confined to the other clone. Not all extrachromosomal determinants show infective transmission when provided with an opportunity. In some instances, the explanation appears to be their immobility. In *Paramecium*, for example, the maternally transmitted determinants of the cortical morphology never show infective heredity, presumably because they reside in the rigid ectoplasm, which is immobile during conjugation (see Fig. 3.3).

The failure of known extrachromosomally inherited differences between varieties of *Epilobium* to migrate across the union between a stock of one variety and a scion of the other must likewise imply that

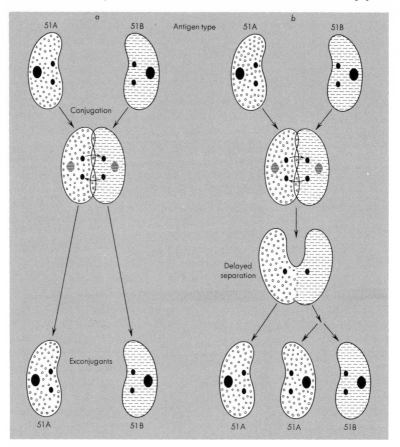

Fig. 6.2. The inheritance of antigen type in stock 51 of variety 4 of *Paramecium aurelia.* (*a*) With the immediate separation of the mates following conjugation, the inheritance is strictly maternal. (*b*) If separation is delayed, so that exchange of extranuclear material occurs, both exconjugant clones may be identical in their antigenic reaction, or one of the exconjugant clones may produce animals with the reaction of both parents. Further details of inheritance in *P. aurelia* are given in Figs. 3.1 and 3.2. After G. H. Beale, *The Genetics of Paramecium aurelia* (Cambridge University Press, 1954).

the determinants are cell-bound. In contrast, many phenotypic differences, for which there is no evidence of extrachromosomal inheritance, are graft-transmissible. (This brings us to a major problem, namely, the relationships and distinctions among viral infection, infective heredity, and sexual heredity, discussion of which is deferred until

Chapter 9.) It means, however, that while infection, as observed in the fungal and *Paramecium* examples, is indicative of an extrachromosomal control, it does not necessarily prove that the control is by hereditary determinants that are normal cell constituents, although where the latter are already indicated by some other criterion, infection provides unambiguous supporting evidence.

Validity of criteria—general conclusions

Chapters 3, 4, 5, and 6 have considered the more important criteria of extrachromosomal heredity and the principles underlying them. These have been considered singly, but in practice all or as many as can be appropriately applied are used jointly to establish a single example of extrachromosomal heredity. It is, therefore, on their combined reliability that their ability to discriminate between chromosomal and extrachromosomal heredity must be judged.

EXAMPLE		CRITERIA						
		1		2			3	4
Variant	Organisms	Reciprocal differences	Non-Mendelian segregations	Somatic segregations	Heterokaryon test	Invasion	Specific mutation	Physical basis
Plastid variegation	Many higher plants	+		+				+
Petite	Yeast		+		+		+	+
Vegitative death	Aspergillus			+	+	+	+̈	
Conidial	glaucus		+			+		
Barrage	Podospora	+	+			+	+̈	
Senescence	anserina	+				+		
Red	Aspergillus			+	+			
Minute	nidulans		+	+			+	
Mating type	Paramecium	+				+		
Serotype	aurelia	+				+		
mi	Neurospora	+			+			+̈
SG	crassa	+					+̈	

Fig. 6.3. The criteria satisfied by particular instances of extrachromosomal heredity. (+ indicates that the criteria have been satisfied.)

The criteria that have been satisfied by particular instances of extrachromosomal heredity have been grouped and are listed in Fig. 6.3. Group 1 includes persistent differences between reciprocal crosses and non-Mendelian segregations—that is, the two types of behavior that do not conform with the known behavior of the chromosomes during gametogenesis and fertilization. Group 2 consists of persistent somatic segregation, reassortment during a heterokaryotic association and infection, all of which are at variance with the integrity of the chromosome complement of mitotically dividing somatic cells. Group 3 concerns the origin of variants by specific induction with a high efficiency, and Group 4 concerns the demonstration of an association between a variant and changes in an extrachromosomal body that possesses physical continuity.

The twelve examples listed in Fig. 6.3 were chosen because of their importance for later discussions and because they are a representative sample of those that have been tested on a variety of criteria. Only two of the twelve, red and vegetative death, fail to show evidence of their extrachromosomal nature on the criteria of Group 1. They are both sexually sterile and therefore the tests cannot be applied. The two criteria in this group are to some extent mutually exclusive. Thus in *Aspergillus*, reciprocal crosses are impossible to perform because all crosses have to be made via the intermediary of heterokaryosis. Therefore, the relative contributions of the two parents to the extrachromosomal material of the progeny cannot be controlled. Hence an extrachromosomal difference between two strains can lead to non-Mendelian segregations, but not to a difference between reciprocal crosses. The same is true, of course, of yeast, for a different reason. In other instances, the two criteria are really inseparable. Thus the complete maternal determination of the phenotype of the progeny of crosses between the *mi* variants and normal and between SG (slow growth) and normal leads to a persistent difference between reciprocal crosses. It also automatically leads to a non-Mendelian segregation, for the variant and normal phenotypes do not segregate in the F_1 progeny in Mendelian proportions, as do all known gene-controlled differences. Similarly, failure of the maternally determined mating or antigen type of reciprocal exconjugant clones of *Paramecium aurelia* to segregate at autogamy is primarily an example of a persistent difference between reciprocal crosses. It is, however, also an example of non-Mendelian segregation. Only the inheritance of barrage satisfies both criteria in independent tests. Thus the modified barrage reaction s^s arises by non-Mendelian segregation in crosses between S and s strains, but the s^s segregants show strict maternal determination when backcrossed to an s strain. It seems, therefore, that these twelve examples satisfy all the criteria of Group 1 that they are capable of being tested for; the only failures are technical ones.

Only one variant, SG, does not satisfy one of the three criteria in Group 2, and there is no evidence that the appropriate tests have ever been tried. All the others behave in one or another of these tests as if their determinants were outside the stable chromosomal complement of mitotically dividing somatic cells. Only one variant, vegetative death, is known to satisfy all three criteria, but this again is not because the other variants are known to have failed the tests, but because the tests have either not yet been made or their outcome not yet reported. Somatic segregation is the only one of the three that could be expected to be satisfied by the plastid variegations of higher plants. The heterokaryon test is clearly inapplicable, and while infection can be tested by grafting a shoot containing only mutant plastids onto a normal rootstock, success could not be expected with the cell-bound plastids. Many other tests in this group are impossible for purely technical reasons. For example, infection in the sense used here cannot be tested for in the nonfilamentous unicellular yeasts and heterokaryon tests cannot be carried out with *Paramecium*.

Only two variants in Fig. 6.3, petite and minute, satisfy the Group 3 criterion; most of the others have arisen only spontaneously or have been induced with a low frequency by the treatments tried so far. However, vegetative death and the modified barrage are in a sense induced with a high frequency.

The criterion of Group 4 is satisfied only by the plastid variegations, petite, and possibly also the *mi* variants, but a combined biochemical and cytological investigation of the other variants, which might uncover their physical basis, has yet to be undertaken.

It has often been found that an unusual genic or chromosomal phenomenon satisfies a particular criterion of extrachromosomal heredity. Foremost among these have been some—for example, paramutation, mitotic recombination, and aneuploidy—that satisfy more than one criterion. But can these unusual phenomena explain the particular combinations of criteria satisfied by the examples in Fig. 6.3? Paramutation can explain the type of non-Mendelian segregation and the specific induction that is confined to the barrage phenomenon, and it could conceivably account for the modification of the phenotype of one strain by another while in heterokaryotic association. But this is not enough to satisfy the particular combination of criteria shown by any of the variants in Fig. 6.3. Mitotic recombination is a possible explanation only if it occurs with a much higher frequency than has been reported so far, and even then it could only produce non-Mendelian segregations and reassortment in a heterokaryon test. None of the variants is based on such a combination of criteria. Aneuploidy, if it is accompanied by preferential segregation, could lead to matrocliny. It could also produce non-Mendelian segregations and some types of somatic segregation. There is ample cytological evidence that aneuploidy is not the explanation of the plastid variegations ascribed to extrachromosomal heredity. In fungi, the cytology is, in general, inadequate to detect aneuploidy. Nevertheless, Etta Käffer has shown that somatic segregation can occur in strains of *A. nidulans*, in which aneuploidy has been ruled out by appropriate breeding tests. Even without this evidence, however, aneuploidy can be ruled out as an explanation of the behavior of the fungal variants, in that all satisfy at least one criterion that cannot be explained by aneuploidy. We may conclude, therefore, that the variants listed in Fig. 6.3 and the many similar examples that are described in Chapters 3, 4, 5, and 6 are proven examples of extrachromosomal heredity.

References

Ephrussi, Boris, and Helene Hottinguer, "Cytoplasmic Constituents of Heredity: On an Unstable Cell State in Yeast," *Cold Spring Harbor Symp. Quant. Biol., 16* (1951), 75.

Faulkner, B. M., and C. F. Arlett, "The 'Minute' Cytoplasmic Variant of *Aspergillus nidulans,*" *Heredity, 19* (1964).

Question

6.1. Design a critical test to distinguish between extrachromosomal determinants of *Paramecium aurelia* borne in the mobile endoplasm and those borne in the cortical ectoplasm.

The Nature of Extrachromosomal
Change

The foregoing chapters presented the case, based on cytological observations and on breeding experiments, for extrachromosomal heredity. My approach has been largely negative and my primary aim has been to show that some regularly observed patterns of inheritance are inexplicable in terms of chromosomal heredity and are hence extrachromosomal in origin. I shall now adopt a more positive, albeit a more speculative, approach and consider the nature of the extrachromosomal system that could produce these results.

Induction of extrachromosomal change

Some extrachromosomal variants have been obtained only once; others occur irregularly with low frequencies that are indistinguishable from the rate of chromosomal gene mutations. Still others, and these are the most interesting, arise with very high frequencies in response to specific external treatments. These variants have no counterpart at the chromosomal level. An examination of their properties is therefore most likely to indicate the ways in which the chromosomal and extrachromosomal systems differ.

Specifically induced changes in phenotype are regularly encountered in which no permanent heritable change in either the chromosomal or the extrachromosomal system can be detected with any certainty. Nevertheless, such changes show a series of grades of persistence that merge imperceptibly with those of the less stable, extrachromosomally inherited changes. They could be intermediate reversible stages in the specific induction of extrachromosomal mutations, or they could be phenotypic mimics of such mutants produced by an environmental modification of the action of a gene or a plasmagene. In either case, an understanding of their properties is essential to an examination of the nature of the specific induction of extrachromosomal mutation.

Phenocopies

The least persistent of the specifically induced phenotypic changes are known as phenocopies. This name was coined by Richard Goldschmidt for the variant phenotypes that he and others produced in *Drosophila melanogaster* by exposing the larvae, at various stages in their development, to high temperatures. The adult flies that develop from the heat-treated larvae resemble to a remarkable degree the phenotypes produced by certain known chromosomal gene mutations. Other treatments, such as sublethal doses of cyanide, silver salts, and quinine, supplied to the larvae through their food, are also effective. All lead to wholesale conversions of the adult phenotype, with efficiencies from 70 to 90 per cent. Furthermore, they are highly specific; the phenotype produced depends on the time of treatment, its duration, and the agent employed. Hence the induction of phenocopies has all the outward properties of the specific induction of extrachromosomal variants. (See Chapter 6.) A property distinguishing phenocopies from all other induced changes, however, is that the effect of the treatment does not extend beyond the life of the treated individual; all the sexual progeny are phenotypically normal (Fig. 7.1). Goldschmidt has equated the process underlying the formation of phenocopies with those produced by a mutant chromosomal gene. The assumption is that the inducing agent interferes with gene action during development in the same way that a mutation interferes with the normal functioning of a gene. He interpreted the importance of the time and duration of the treatment in determining the type of phenocopy obtained as indicating a sensitive period in larval development, when a particular phenotypic upset is most easily produced by interfering with a specific phase of development. This sensitive period presumably coincides with the time of maximum or most critical contribution of the gene, whose activity is interfered with by the treatment, to normal development.

The failure of the phenocopy to appear in its own sexual progeny is the principal reason for preferring an explanation based on a modification in the function of the hereditary material rather than in the hereditary material itself. This reason, however, does not exclude an induced change in the function of plasmagenes as an explanation. Nor does it exclude the type of extrachromosomal change that led to the appearance of the minute variant in *Aspergillus nidulans*. This specifically induced variant segregates persistently in all the somatic cells of a colony, but it never appears in its own sexual progeny, which are invariably normal in phenotype. The minute variant would, therefore, be as transitory as a phenocopy, except that the organism in which it occurs can be propagated almost indefinitely by somatic cells. As a result, the original minute variant has been maintained for over seven years. According to Goldschmidt's definition, minute is a phenocopy, but it is also a persistently segregating extrachromosomal variant, whose exclusion from the sexual progeny can be explained by selection during the development of the germ line. (See Chapter 12.) It can be argued that minute is not a heritable variant, in that it is not transmitted through the sexual stage. But does not persistence through veg-

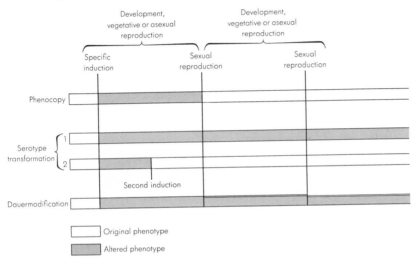

Fig. 7.1. The difference in persistence of the specifically induced phenocopies, serotype transformations, and dauermodifications. Serotype transformations are not affected by sexual reproduction (1), but they can be reversed or change to a new serotype by a second induction (2). Dauermodifications do survive sexual reproduction, but, although only the modified individuals are bred from, the proportion of the latter becomes progressively smaller in successive sexual progenies.

etative and asexual propagations constitute inheritance in organisms in which these are the principal, or, as in imperfect fungi, the only methods of reproduction? Are then phenocopies and minute one and the same? Do they differ merely in the technical possibilities of the organisms in which they occur? Certainly this explanation should not be dismissed out of hand. For the present, however, we can only note that minute satisfies a number of criteria of extrachromosomal heredity, but it can be described as a phenocopy of a well-known class of gene mutations that produce a compact colonial growth.

Serotype transformations

The serotype transformations in *Paramecium aurelia* (Fig. 7.1) are more persistent than phenocopies, in that they are inherited by the sexual progeny. Within a stock of varieties 1 and 4 of *P. aurelia*, there exist a number of different serological strains and, as we have seen in Chapter 4, these show extrachromosomal inheritance following conjugation between two different serotypes of the same stock. Tracy M. Sonneborn and G. H. Beale have analyzed the range of serotypes that may occur in a single homozygous clone in response to different external treatments. For example, stock 51 of variety 4 may exist as *A,B,C,D,E,G,H*, and *J* serotypes, and stock 29 as *A,B,C,D,F,H*, and *J*. Changes or transformations of one serotype to another are obtained in response to sublethal doses of specific antisera and modifications of temperature and diet. Not only do these treatments produce wholesale transformation of all members of a clone subjected to them, but the direction of the change may be controlled. A specific treatment will always change a particular serotype to a certain other type. In variety 4, serotype *D* of stock 29 is transformed to serotype *B* by the action of antiserum *D* if the temperature is 32°C., but to serotype *H* if it is 20°C. Under suitable conditions either transformation is stable, but transformation back to *D* may still be achieved under other conditions. In variety 1, serotype *S* is found between 10° to 18°C., the *C* serotype between 18° and 27°C., and the *D* serotype from 25° to 35°C. However, the exact boundaries of the various temperature ranges vary from stock to stock. In stock 90, serotype *G* occurs from 10° to 30°C., while in stock 60 it occurs only between 20° and 25°C. At temperatures on the borderline between the ranges characteristic for two different states, for example, 25°C., in stock 60, it is possible to maintain parallel cultures that are either serotype *D* or *G* for long periods. At rare intervals, there may be a change from serotype *D* to *G* or the reverse, but these changes, if they occur, are abrupt. Intermediate conditions in which both *D* and *G* coexist in the same animal are confined to about two fissions during which the change is taking place.

Chromosomally borne genes undoubtedly play a role in the control of serotype formation. Serotype *A* of stock 51, while similar, is not identical to serotype *A* of stock 29. The difference is due to allelic genes at the same locus, that of stock 51 being dominant. Similar allelic differences have also been demonstrated at other serotype-determining loci in other stocks. For this reason, Sonneborn believes that stock 51 and stock 29 carry, at different loci, genes for serotype specificity. Eight different loci would be required on this basis to account for the eight known serotypes of stock 51, and seven loci for the seven known serotypes of stock 29. Thus in a strain of stock 51 that was serotype *A*, only the gene at the *A* locus would be active; the genes at the other seven loci would be inhibited in some way. Since the environment can bring about transformations, the environment must, of course, determine which locus, out of all the possibilities, is active and which loci are inactive. The genotype, on the other hand, determines the range of alternative serotypes that the environment can call forth in this way. Thus the extrachromosomal role might merely be that of an intermediary between genotype and the environment. The different extrachromosomal states would be determined partly by the environment and partly by the past history of the extrachromosomal material, and they in turn would determine which of a range of gene-controlled serotypes was expressed. But a more active role for the extrachromosomal system is compatible with the evidence, for the genes that control the serotypes could operate by conferring specificity on nonspecific plasmagenes. Equally compatible are some proposed explanations in which extrachromosomal hereditary material plays no part. Such explanations involve an equilibrium system with alternative, mutually exclusive pathways that can be switched from one to another by changes in the environment; the only components in this system are the products of chromosomal genes.

The essential difference between a phenocopy and a serotype transformation is that the latter is not reversed by sexual reproduction. Instead, it shows strict maternal transmission. It can be reversed, however, during vegetative multiplication by a suitable external stimulus (Fig. 7.1). But are these differences any more than a reflection of the different levels of organization in the organisms in which they occur? A paramecium, whether reproducing vegetatively or by sexual reproduction, divides all of its extrachromosomal material between its daughter cells. Only the nuclear behavior is obviously different between these two modes of reproduction (see Fig. 3.1). There is, therefore, no reason why a phenotypic change that depends on a modification of the extrachromosomal system should persist through one type of reproduction without also passing through the other—unless, of course, the environmental stimulus that brought about the initial modification is also reversed. In *Drosophila*, the presumptive germ cells and soma are separated early in development. Subsequent development is then virtually confined to the activity of somatic cells. For a stimulus applied during this period of development to affect the adult phenotype, it must modify the activity of the somatic cells. Hence any change resulting from the stimulus, no matter what its nature, will probably be confined to the somatic cells. It will not generally, therefore, be transmitted through the gametes. Furthermore, once a particular stage in the development of the soma of an individual has been modified by the stimulus, it is permanent, because that particular stage occurs only once in the life of an individual. Hence the difference in the permanence of a phenocopy and a serotype transformation could follow directly from the difference in the development of the organisms in which they occur. There is no need to postulate a difference in the nature of any change that might occur in the hereditary material.

Dauermodifications

Dauermodifications have been defined as transient, environmentally induced changes in the extrachromosomal system, decreasing in penetrance and expressivity in succeeding generations in the absence of the inducing stimulus, but nevertheless persisting in some of the offspring for several, and sometimes many, generations. During the period of persistence of the induced phenotypic change, it is transmitted matroclinally. Thus dauermodifications form a link between phenocopies at the one extreme, and persistent extrachromosomal mutants at the other (Fig. 7.1).

Dauermodifications have been obtained in species ranging from Protista, particularly *Paramecium* and *Arcella*, through insects such as *Drosophila*, to higher plants, notably *Antirrhinum* and *Phaseolus*. The method of induction is similar in all cases. The organism is grown in an unfavorable environment produced by the presence of sublethal doses of poison, extreme temperatures, excessive ion concentrations, starvation, and antisera, all of which induce a phenotypic change. After varying periods of time, the treated organism is returned to a normal environment.

A typical example is the abnormal leaf development induced in *Phaseolus vulgaris* by treatment with a 0.75 per cent solution of chloral hydrate. The first generation of sexual progeny after treatment gave 73 per cent affected plants. Although in this and in all subsequent generations, only the affected plants were used as parents, by the seventh generation no affected plant was observed among 200 progeny examined. Nevertheless, even as late as the fourth generation, half the plants were still affected. Clearly, this is no temporary modification of gene action. Nor is the extrachromosomal role one of a passive intermediary between gene and environment—because of the duration of the effect after the withdrawal of the stimulus, and its matroclinal transmission while it lasts. An extrachromosomally inherited change that has powers of self-perpetuation but that, for some reason, lacks the persistency of a stable mutant must be involved. To persist as long as it does, material with genetic continuity must be altered; to show matroclinal inheritance, this material must be extrachromosomal; to be lost ultimately it must be gradually replaced by the homologous material found in a normal cell or organism. This leaves two alternatives: either backmutation gradually restores the changed extrachromosomal material to normal, or there is a cumulative selection for any unchanged extrachromosomal material that has survived the original induction. According to both explanations the treated individuals and their abnormal maternal progenies possess both mutant and normal homologues of an extrachromosomal determinant, since the normal homologues either remain unchanged during the induction or arise subsequently by backmutation. That is, the treated organisms and their abnormal progenies are variegated as are, for example, newly arisen instances of plastid mutations. Selection of individuals, cells, and gametes that, as a result of somatic segregation, contain the highest proportions of the normal homologues then leads to a progressive loss of the mutant homologues and the restoration of a pure breeding, normal phenotype.

The advantage of this interpretation is that it explains not only the properties of dauermodifications but many of the properties of extrachromosomally inherited variants. The important feature of the interpretation is that the reversion of a dauermodification is not due to the instability of an altered extrachromosomal determinant but to the somatic instability of the induced heteroplasmic state. All degrees of persistence of a phenotypic change can be explained on the heteroplasmic model by assuming different intensities of selection for or against the mutant component. But more appropriate models can explain the lesser degrees of persistence.

Enzymatic adaptation

The phenomenon of enzyme adaptation, the change in enzyme content of cells brought about by specific environmental changes, has been regarded by many as the mechanism probably underlying the less stable phenotypic changes, for example, phenocopies. The constitution of the substrate on which a micro-organism is grown commonly has a marked effect on its enzyme system. The presence of a particular substrate may lead an organism to produce a previously undetected enzyme activity that can utilize it. Hence a change in the environment can produce a wholesale change in the phenotype of organisms exposed to it, as judged by their enzyme activity. One of the most carefully studied examples, largely as the result of the investigations of Jacques Monod and his collaborators, is the induced synthesis of the enzyme β-galactosidase in the bacterium *Escherichia coli*. β-galactosidase is formed by bacteria grown in the presence of lactose, because this enzyme is necessary for the utilization of lactose. A number of other galactosides that do not provide a substitute for the enzyme, for example, thio methyl-β-D-galactoside, will nevertheless induce its formation. Upon addition of an inducer at a sufficiently high concentration to a growing bacterial culture, the bacteria almost immediately begin to make enzyme at the maximum rate. Furthermore, under these conditions there is a uniform distribution of enzyme among the individual bacteria present as early as five minutes after the addition of the inducer. At low inducer concentrations, the cultures consist essentially of individual bacteria that are either making enzyme at the maximum rate or not making it at all. That is, the uninduced bacteria make the transition to the induced state as the result of a random single event. Thus the process bears a close resemblance to mutation. Unlike mutation, however, the induction system requires the continued presence of a low concentration of inducer to maintain the difference between the induced and uninduced states. The enzyme is gradually lost after the inducer is withdrawn by a process of dilution during cell multiplication.

A detailed analysis of the effects of withdrawing galactose from yeast cells, which had been induced to hydrolyze this sugar, has been carried out by A. M. Campbell and S. I. Spiegelman. By examining successive buds produced by an adapted cell growing in the absence of galactose, they found that deadapted buds were first produced at the fifth division, and thereafter increased in frequency at each successive division. This rate of deadaptation can be interpreted on the basis of approximately 100 particles (which may be the enzyme itself, or some complex containing the enzyme) in the adapted cell, if we assume that the particles do not multiply after the removal of galactose and that they are randomly distributed between cells at each division. With this initial frequency, the particles are sufficiently diluted by the fifth division for cells containing none to arise with the observed frequency.

By no means do all enzymes require external induction before their activity may be detected. Strains of the same species may differ, in that one strain will possess a particular enzyme activity irrespective of the substrate, while another will show it only if induced to do so. When such differences occur in strains that are amenable to genetic analyses, they are invariably found to be due to different chromosomal alleles. The principal components of enzymatic induction are, therefore, the possibility of induction determined by the chromosomal genes and the stimulus for induction provided by the environment. They are identical with the components of serotype transformations. They differ only in their persistence following the withdrawal of the stimulus. But this is enough to rule out enzymatic adaptation as a sufficient explanation of serotype transformations, although it clearly could be an important component. On the other hand, induction, as a model of short-lived, environmentally modifiable gene action, is a sufficient explanation of phenocopying. Enzymatic induction also has many similarities to heritable extrachromosomal mutations, for example, their specific induction and their ability to produce segregation within a clone of genotypically identical cells. But it must be made perfectly clear that enzymatic induction does not satisfy a single criterion of extrachromosomal heredity, as used in Chapters 3, 4, 5, and 6. It is, in consequence, a satisfactory explanation only for those induced phenotypic changes that themselves fail to satisfy the criteria.

Extrachromosomal mutants

The environmentally induced phenotypic changes that we have now examined form a graded and overlapping series of persistence, from enzymatic induction and phenocopies at one extreme to dauermodifications at the other. With increasing persistence the evidence for the participation of extrachromosomal hereditary material in these changes becomes stronger until there is no real distinction between the more persistent dauermodifications and many extrachromosomal mutants. To what extent, however, does this series reflect different degrees of change in the extrachromosomal hereditary material?

A normal yeast cell grown under anaerobic conditions, at high temperatures, or in the presence of acridine dyes has the phenotype and enzyme activity of a petite variant. Thus the initial, and presumably adaptive, response to these treatments is to produce a petite phenotype; but the change is temporary—it is a phenocopy. There is, however, a critical stage in the treatment beyond which the phenotypic change is no longer reversible when the cells are returned to normal conditions and many, if not all, cells have become permanently petite. From this stage on it is a permanent, stable, extrachromosomal mutant. Thus a treatment that produces a temporary change in phenotype may, if prolonged, produce an extrachromosomal mutation. To take another example, the absence of light, in making the plastids of *Euglena mesnili* redundant, also leads to a reduction of their number. This reduction is initially reversible, but if the treatment is continued all visible plastid structure is lost, and an irreversible change in the extrachromosomal complement of the cell is produced. Hence, in both examples, an initial adjustment in cell metabolism, in response to an environmental stimulus, is pushed to a point of no return. That is, the stable variants represent the last and only irreversible stage in a sequence of changes induced by the treatments.

Since at least one normal determinant must be present in a cell for others to be produced, the last normal homologue must be lost from a cell lineage for it to pass from an initial reversible change in phenotype to an irreversible change. As long as one normal homologue remains the change is prospectively reversible and, therefore, a dauermodification. Does this model fit the facts of specific mutagenesis?

The best known of the specific mutagens—acridine dyes—inhibit the synthesis of those respiratory enzymes that are lacking or reduced in concentration in the induced respiratory mutants. While, however, this inhibition may be an initial stage in the induction of the petite mutant, the respiratory enzymes of some species of yeast, which cannot be induced to produce petite mutants, are also inhibited by these dyes. In these species, therefore, the dyes produce only phenocopies. Hence mutagenesis does not necessarily follow the inhibition of the syntheses.

Boris Ephrussi and Helene Hottinguer have shown that a cell of the yeast *Saccaromyces cereviseae*, exposed to acridines for only a short period, will produce both normal and mutant buds, and that some of the normal buds, without further treatment, will occasionally produce mutant as well as normal buds. After more prolonged treatment, however, the treated cell will produce only mutant buds, and these in turn will give only mutant buds. There are, therefore, intermediate stages in the induction, in which a single cell retains its ability to produce a normal bud while gaining the ability to produce a mutant bud. This must imply that the extrachromosomal determinants of a normal and petite phenotype can coexist in the same cell during the induction of the mutant, and that there are a number of intermediate steps in the change of the extrachromosomal content of a normal cell to that of a stable petite cell.

Earlier in this chapter, the initial response of cells to specific mutagens was likened to an enzymatic adaptation induced by a new environment. The final response, namely, the appearance of the stable mutant, however, is certainly not adaptive, for in no case does the mutant show a superiority over normal cells under the conditions inducing its appearance. We can therefore recognize a number of stages in the specific induction of an extrachromosomal mutant (Fig. 7.2). The initial stages are similar to enzymatic induction, and they are as temporary as phenocopies. Later stages are partially reversible because some, but not all, of the normal representatives of a determinant have been lost or altered. The final stage is as nonadaptive, stable, and persistent as any gene mutation.

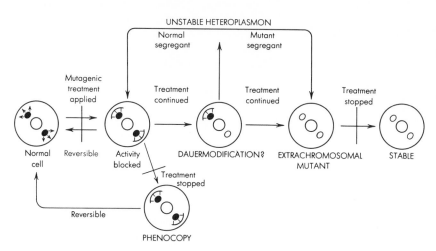

Fig. 7.2. Hypothetical relationships between the various specific, environmentally induced changes. The essential features of this scheme are: (1) that phenocopy production is a preliminary stage to all these changes; (2) that dauermodifications are an intermediate stage between phenocopies and extrachromosomal mutations; (3) that phenocopies are reversible because only functional changes are involved; and (4) that dauermodifications are more persistent but also reversible because, although they involve mutations, not all the homologues of a determinant are affected.

The nature of extrachromosomal mutations

It has long been claimed that the extrachromosomal components of heredity may undergo permanent changes analogous to the mutations of chromosomal genes. What is the nature of these changes? Looking first at a visible extrachromosomal system, the plastids, we find two distinct kinds of change described as mutations. First, there are the mutant strains of *Euglena* that no longer possess any plastids. In these mutants, the genetic continuity of the plastids has been permanently broken. Second, there are the mutants of higher plants that possess functionally or morphologically modified plastids. Here the genetic continuity of the plastid is retained, but the genetic information it carries is defective. Turning to another visible model, namely, the cortical determinants of the external morphology of *Paramecium aurelia*, we find that the phenotypic difference between monsters and normal animals can be traced to the duplication or deletion of particular cortical regions. Thus among the plastid mutants and the morphological mutants of *P. aurelia* we can recognize three categories of extrachromosomal change. By analogy with chromosomal changes, these categories are equivalent to deletions, structural changes, and duplications.

Loss of or change in a determinant

Since mitochondria are the carriers of certain respiratory enzymes, and since the petite mutant lacks these enzymes, it was originally suggested by Boris Ephrussi that the mutation might arise because of the physical loss of the mitochondria or some other entity that participates in the synthesis of the enzymes. It was subsequently found, however, that the sedimentable fractions isolated from homogenates of respiratory mutants could not be distinguished from the corresponding fractions of normal yeast by their gross analytical characteristics. Furthermore, Y. Yotsuyanagi convincingly showed that the respiratory mutants do contain mitochondria. Hence the physical loss of mitochondria in the mutant can be ruled out on both physical, chemical, and cytological grounds. More recent electron micrographs have, in fact, shown that the mitochondria present in the mutant cells are morphologically abnormal. Thus the mutant possesses functionally and structurally modified mitochondria. If, therefore, the mitochondria are the bearers of their own extrachromosomal determinants, then the mutation involves structural changes in the bearers rather than their deletion. It could still be argued, however, that the structural and functional changes in the mitochondria are only secondary effects of a change in some other extrachromosomal entity. If this is the case, the physical loss of the extrachromosomal entity has not been ruled out as the cause of the mutation.

Breeding experiments have done much to resolve this difficulty. In crosses between neutral petite and normal cells, neutral petite never appears in the progeny (see Fig. 5.1). This behavior is in agreement with the origin of petite by the physical loss of a determinant. Suppressive petite, however, appears in the progeny of such crosses; indeed, the majority of the progeny in some circumstances inherit the petite phenotype (see Chapter 5). If suppressive petite merely lacked a determinant, copulation with a normal cell prior to sexual reproduction would, at most, reduce the level of the determinant by half. Why, therefore, does the petite phenotype predominate among the zygotes and increase in frequency with time? (See Fig. 5.1.) Clearly, suppression cannot operate by dilution. This conclusion also applies to mutant phenotypes that can be transmitted to normal strains by heterokaryotic association or infection. Small inocula of some suppressive variants, for example, vegetative death, will successfully transmit their phenotype to a considerably larger colony of a normal strain with which they are in contact. It is difficult to see how the basis for such variants could be the absence of a determinant that is present in the normal strain (see Fig. 6.1).

Not all extrachromosomal mutants, however, are suppressive. On the contrary, some are suppressed by the normal strains. For example, the fertility of nonsexual strains may be restored by heterokaryotic association with a normal strain. Such variants could, therefore, merely lack a determinant that is present in the normal strain. If the same arguments are applied to the petite variant, the neutral form could be classified as a loss mutation and the suppressive form as a mutant with an altered determinant. Unfortunately, there is insufficient information about the relationship of these two forms of petite to know whether such a classification is likely.

The breeding experiments confirm that some extrachromosomal mutations result from an alteration in a determinant, rather than from its physical loss. Where an altered determinant cannot be demonstrated by breeding tests, it does not necessarily follow that the loss of a determinant is involved. Thus a mutant determinant that is recessive to its normal homologue and rapidly suppressed by it whenever both are present in the same cell would be indistinguishable from a loss mutation in the breeding test described. In chromosomal heredity, there are standard tests for detecting a loss mutation or deletion—one of the simplest is of inability to backmutate. Unfortunately, there have been no systematic investigations of the backmutation rate of any extrachromosomal mutant. For many variants, particularly the persistently segregating variants of fungi and the plastid variegations of higher plants, it would, in general, be almost impossible to distinguish between backmutation and somatic segregation. Peter Michaelis, however, has described cells containing both abnormal and normal plastids in leaves that are borne on branches containing only abnormal plastids. He has claimed, therefore, that these normal plastids must have arisen by backmutation. Most authors, quite naturally, have stressed only the stability of the extrachromosomal variants that they have described, but it would be unwise to deduce from this their inability to backmutate. The question, therefore, of the existence of extrachromosomal mutants that have lost all representatives of a particular determinant must remain open.

Chemical basis

What, in fact, is the material whose alteration or loss constitutes an extrachromosomal mutation? It is generally agreed that an alteration in the nucleotide sequence of deoxyribonucleic acid (DNA) constitutes a hereditary change at the chromosomal level. (See *The Mechanics of Inheritance* and *Gene Action* in this series.) On the other hand, viruses containing ribonucleic acid (RNA) but no DNA also mutate, and the mutant forms are persistent. Hence heritable modifications can occur in RNA, presumably by alterations in the pattern of nucleotides (see *Gene Action*). There are, therefore, two known substances, DNA and RNA, that can possess genetic continuity. The presence of either in an extrachromosomal entity would be presumptive evidence that the latter could be a bearer of genetic information.

There have been increasingly persistent claims that DNA is present in structures such as plastids and mitochondria. Its detection by chemical analysis is fraught with many difficulties, the most important of which is excluding the possibility that these structures have absorbed DNA from damaged chromosomes or other extraneous sources during the extraction processes. Nevertheless, the case for its presence, based on chemical analysis, while not conclusive, is certainly suggestive. The evidence from electron microscopic studies is contradictory. Some studies have demonstrated the presence of DNA fibers, others have failed to do so. On balance, however, it seems likely that DNA is a constituent of mitochondria and plastids. It may well be, therefore, that plasmagene mutations result from the modification of extrachromosomal DNA.

Although there is no indication that DNA is present in other extrachromosomal bodies, the possibility cannot be dismissed at present. RNA, on the other hand, has been claimed to be a constituent of many extrachromosomal entities. It is undoubtedly a major component of microsomes, and mitochondria may contain it in amounts up to 3 per cent of the protein content, but they may also be virtually free of RNA. The protein that enters into the structure of extrachromosomal bodies is another possible possessor of genetic continuity. In the absence of DNA, however, RNA must be the principal candidate for this role because of its proven ability to act in this capacity in certain viruses.

Still, by no means can all the RNA present in a cell be considered for the role of extrachromosomal hereditary material. Much of it is chromosomal or nucleolar in origin. Furthermore, much of it shows a rapid turnover and hence is in no sense a permanent cellular component or a constituent of cell structures. Clearly, there are many forms of RNA, and their differing roles in cell hereditary and metabolism are only just being sorted out. Their interrelationships will provide the basis of a later discussion in Chapter 11.

Although at present there is little undisputed evidence concerning the nature of the hereditary material responsible for extrachromosomal inheritance, examination and investigation of its fundamental properties need not be postponed. Most, if not all, of the fundamental properties of chromosomal hereditary material were established long before there was any undisputed evidence about the nature of the chromosomal hereditary material.

Number of sites

The variety of phenotypic changes showing extrachromosomal inheritance that have now been described in a single strain, let alone in a single species, suggests either that there are many sites in the extrachromosomal system at which mutations may occur or, alternatively, that many phenotypically distinct changes can occur as a result of different mutations at the same site. That is, by analogy with the chromosomal system, there are either multiple alleles or multiple loci in the extrachromosomal system. In maize, for example, three alleles are required to account for extrachromosomally inherited plastid abnormalities and male sterility, if these are all controlled by the same locus. If, however, plastid abnormalities and male sterility are due to changes at different sites, two loci, each with two alleles, are required. But, as we shall see later, independently arising male sterilities in maize are often functionally different; therefore, either there are many alleles at the male sterility locus or there is more than one locus controlling male sterility. In one strain of the fungus *Aspergillus nidulans*, for example, at least six phenotypically distinct extrachromosomally inherited variants have been obtained. Including all the variants in all the different strains of this species, the total is more than twice as high. Since each new mutagenic treatment appears to produce its own specific phenotypic change, there seems to be no limit, at the moment, to the new alleles or loci that must be postulated in the extrachromosomal system of this fungus. Further discussion of the extrachromosomal system must, therefore, recognize its probable multi-allelic or multilocular character.

References

Beale, G. H., "The Role of the Cytoplasm in Antigen Determination in *Paramecium aurelia*," *Proc. Roy. Soc. (London)*, Ser. B, *148* (1958), 308.

Goldschmidt, Richard, *Theoretical Genetics*. Berkeley and Los Angeles: University of California Press, 1955.

Jollos, V., "Dauermodifications," *Handb. Vererb.* (1939), 1-100.

Monod, Jacques, "Remarks on the Mechanism of Enzyme Induction," in *Enzymes: Units of Biological Structure and Function*, O. H. Gaebler, ed. (New York: Academic Press, Inc., 1956), p. 7.

Questions

7.1. The induction of enzymes does not satisfy the criteria of extrachromosomal heredity; enzyme induction cannot, therefore, explain any example of extrachromosomal heredity that satisfies these criteria. Discuss this statement.

7.2. Explain why the existence of mutants that suppress their wild-type homologues in a heteroplasmon make it necessary to postulate that mutants may arise by a change in function of an extrachromosomal plasmagene rather than by the physical loss of a plasmagene.

Eight

The Basis of Extrachromosomal

Segregation

The replication of centrioles, kinetosomes, and the single plastids of many lower organisms, as well as their distribution between daughter cells at cell division, has the orderliness of chromosome behavior (see Chapters 2 and 3). But this is not true for all extrachromosomal entities. It is often necessary to assume that the distribution of plasmagenes at cell division lacks the precision normally associated with chromosomally borne genes. This is particularly so for the extrachromosomal determinants of differences that show somatic segregation (see Chapter 5). The cause and consequences of the somatic segregation of plasmagenes can be easily illustrated by reference to the simplest model that allows segregation, namely, one in which each cell receives two homologues of a plasmagene at its initiation.

A model of somatic segregation

Let us suppose that each cell contains two homologues of an extrachromosomal determinant A. Each cell will receive two homologues at its initiation and pass on two to its daughter cells at cell division. Before each cell divides, therefore, either the two homologues must divide to give four or they must generate two more homologues. In such a cell, one homologue A mutates to an alternative form a, thus changing the cell constitution to Aa. In this model the change from A to

91

a represents any one of the kinds of extrachromosomal mutation, including a physical loss, which is discussed in Chapter 7. Prior to cell division, its constitution will become *AAaa.* If the distribution of homologues at cell division is regular—that is, if it follows the same rules as the chromosomes—both daughter cells will have the constitution *Aa* (Fig. 8.1a). If their distribution is irregular—that is, if the two *A* homologues pass to one daughter cell and the two *a* homologues to the other—the daughter cell will have the constitutions *AA* and *aa,* respectively. They will have segregated (Fig. 8.1b).

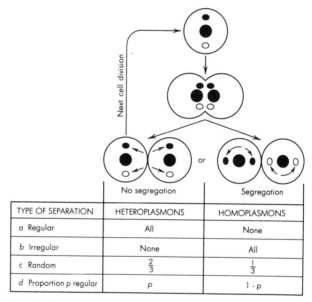

TYPE OF SEPARATION	No segregation HETEROPLASMONS	Segregation HOMOPLASMONS
a Regular	All	None
b Irregular	None	All
c Random	$\frac{2}{3}$	$\frac{1}{3}$
d Proportion p regular	p	1 - p

Fig. 8.1. The two kinds of division that can occur in a heteroplasmic cell containing one normal and one mutant homologue of a determinant, both of which replicate prior to division. The relative frequencies with which these two occur depend on the type of separation.

Let us now suppose that the distribution is neither invariably regular nor invariably irregular, but sometimes one and sometimes the other. For example, let us suppose that it is random. Each homologue will then have an equal opportunity to have any one of the three remaining homologues as its partner. Hence if an *A* homologue passes to one daughter cell, the probability that it will be accompanied by the other *A* is one-third, and the probability that it will be accompanied by one of the two *a* homologues is two-thirds. Random distribution, therefore, leads to one-third regular and two-thirds irregular separation. The relative frequencies of daughter cells with the constitutions *AA, Aa,* and *aa* will, therefore, be $\frac{1}{6}$, $\frac{4}{6}$, and $\frac{1}{6}$, respectively (Fig. 8.1c).

We have assumed a random distribution, but this is only one of many possibilities. A more general model would be to assume a proportion p of regular separations and a proportion $(1 - p)$ of irregular separations. The expected frequency of daughter cells with the constitutions AA, Aa, and aa would then be $\frac{1}{2}(1 - p)$, p, and $\frac{1}{2}(1 - p)$, respectively (Fig. 8.1d).

Our simple model may be elaborated in a variety of ways. For example, we could consider more than two homologues per cell, and the consequences of successive generations of cell division. Peter Michaelis has considered both in his attempt to fit a satisfactory model to the observed somatic segregation of plastid differences in *Epilobium*. He has, for example, derived the expected segregation pattern for six successive cell divisions following a mutation in one homologue of a cell containing from $n = 5$ to $n = 5,000$ homologues of an extrachromosomal determinant. The general conclusions that may be drawn from this extensive model-building may be summarized as follows.

The larger the number, n, of homologues per cell, the larger the average number of cell divisions before cells containing only mutant homologues arise. Let us take a simple illustration. In our original model (Fig. 8.1c), one-sixth of the daughter cells are expected, on the average, to contain only mutant homologues if their distribution is random. If a cell contained four A homologues and one mutated to a, the three types of daughter cell that could arise would have the constitutions $AAAA$, $AAAa$, and $AAaa$. It would require at least one further round of cell division for cells of the constitution $aaaa$ to arise.

Unless the distribution of normal and mutant homologues at cell division is invariably regular (Fig. 8.1a), the proportion of cells containing both normal and mutant homologues will decrease with every round of cell division. The situation is analogous to inbreeding. For example, on our original model, the expected proportion of cells with constitution Aa after one cell division is two-thirds if the distribution is random. The remaining one-third is equally divided between the constitutions AA and aa, and these will give only AA and aa daughter cells, respectively, at the next cell division. The cells with the constitution Aa, however, will again give two-thirds daughter cells with the same constitution. Hence after two cell divisions, only two-thirds of the original two-thirds of the cells with the Aa constitution will still have this constitution. Therefore, providing the distribution is random, each round of cell division reduces the Aa class of cells by two-thirds. After g rounds of cell divisions, the frequency of this class will thus be $(\frac{2}{3})^g$.

Application to plastid segregations in Epilobium

Michaelis has made extensive tests of the suitability of his theoretical models. In the development of the leaves of variegated plants, for example, he has determined the cell divisions at which cell lineages arise containing only abnormal plastids. He has also made counts of the relative numbers of normal and abnormal plastids in pairs of daughter cells of the palisade of variegated leaves. His conclusions from these and many similar observations are that a model based on the assumptions (1) that the plasmagenes controlling the phenotype of the plastids are distributed at random at cell division and (2) that the number of homologues of the plasmagenes per cell is about the same as the mean number of plastids (about twelve) provides a satisfactory explanation of the quantitative segregation of plastid differences during mitotic cell divisions.

While there is a good over-all agreement between the model, which is based on a number of assumptions and the observed segregation of plastids in *Epilobium*, this agreement does not verify the individual assumptions. Nevertheless, this model is the most useful in considering those cases of somatic segregation where the physical basis of the segregation is unknown. In such cases, breeding experiments provide ample evidence of irregular distribution of determinants at cell division, for we may infer from the observed phenotypic segregations a corresponding segregation among the determinants. The persistently segregating variants of filamentous fungi, such as *Aspergillus*, show that somatic segregation of their determinants occurs when hyphae branch and when asexual spores are produced (see Figs. 5.3, 5.4, and 5.5). Thus clones initiated from single hyphae or from single asexual spores of these variants produce hyphae and spores that in turn give clones containing every possible phenotype from a pure breeding normal to a pure breeding mutant. In fact, it is often possible to obtain clones with the whole range of phenotypes by germinating the asexual spores produced as successive buds of a single cell.

Application to persistent segregation in Aspergillus

In *Aspergillus*, the production of asexual spores is generative; the mother cell retains its integrity while budding off successive daughter cells, the spores. The spores are, therefore, small samples of the relatively very large extrachromosomal mass produced by the mother cell. On the simplest model that will permit segregation among the spores produced by a single mother cell, each mother cell must receive two homologues, one normal A and one mutant a. Prior to the production of asexual spores, these homologues must multiply until there are m per cell. We will assume an equal rate of multiplication of the two forms, so that when spore production commences there are $\frac{1}{2}m$ A and $\frac{1}{2}m$ a homologues. If, therefore, the spores receive only one homologue, half will receive the A form and half the a form. However, while this would lead to a segregation, the ability to segregate would not be transmitted by the spores. To transmit this ability, the asexual spores must receive at least two homologues. If the two homologues were a random sample of an infinite number ($m = \infty$) present in the mother cell, the frequency of spores with the constitution AA, Aa, and aa would be $\frac{1}{4}$, $\frac{1}{2}$, and $\frac{1}{4}$, respectively. These expectations are the expansion of the binomial expression $(p + q)^n$, where p (the frequency of A homologues) $= q$ (the frequency of a homologues) $= \frac{1}{2}$; and n (the number of homologues per spore) $= 2$. In practice, m will be finite, hence the more complex hypergeometric distribution is more appropriate than the binomial. However, if m is large in relation to n, the simpler binomial distribution is a good approximation. For example, with $n = 2$ and $m = 50$, the deviation is less than 1 per cent. If the distribution of homologues is, therefore, random, we can predict the segregation among asexual spores produced by a heteroplasmic mother cell for any proportion of homologues ($p : q$) and for any number of homologues per spore (n) by expanding the appropriate binomial expression.

One other point we should note is that if segregation occurs during asexual spore production, the number of classes of spores (k) is always equal to $n + 1$. In general, the asexual spores of the somatically unstable variants of *Aspergillus* cannot be grouped into distinct classes. Thus if the spores are judged on the phenotypes of the colonies they produce on germination, there must be a continuous spectrum of spore constitutions (see Chapter 5). This suggests that n is large. In all cases, n is at least 2, since the ability to segregate is always transmitted by some, if not by most asexual spores.

The asexual spores of the red variant have been grouped into a minimum of seven classes on the following basis. Random samples of the spores of this variant were germinated, and the asexual progenies of the colonies produced were classified into red and nonred phenotypes. The relative frequencies of red segregants fall into at least seven significantly different classes whose means are 0, 13, 40, 57, 66, 79, and 92 per cent red segregants. Each class among the asexual progenies presumably coincides with at least one different spore constitution in the initial random sample of asexual spores. And since there are seven classes, we must postulate at least seven different proportions of normal to mutant homologues in the asexual spores. Thus the 0 per cent class must arise from spores containing only normal homologues, and the 92 per cent class from spores containing mainly mutant homologues, but at least one normal homologue. The 100 per cent class has not been recovered; this would arise from spores containing only mutant homologues. If this possible but unrecovered class is included, $k = 8$, and hence $n = 7$. The constitutions of the seven recovered classes of spores are, therefore, respectively $7 : 0, 6 : 1, 5 : 2, 4 : 3$, $3 : 4, 2 : 5$, and $1 : 6$ normal to mutant homologues.

If we accept the idea that eight classes of spores are possible, we can estimate their relative frequencies in random samples of spores. Such a sample of 25 spores is classified in Fig. 8.2. On the basis of this classification, the frequencies of normal and mutant homologues (p and q) can be estimated. Out of a total of $25 \times 7 = 175$ homologues in the initial 25 spores, 88 are normal and 87 are mutant. Hence $p = q = \frac{1}{2}$. Since $n = 7$, we can calculate the expected frequency of spores in the eight classes, assuming random distribution of homologues by expanding the binomial expression $(\frac{1}{2} + \frac{1}{2})^7$. The agreement of the expectations with the observations is good. Our model, therefore, is an adequate representation of the segregation of homologues in a heteroplasmic mother cell during asexual spore production.

Three minimal conditions for the persistent somatic segregation of extrachromosomally inherited differences have now been established:

(1) The regular presence of more than one homologue of the determinant in each cell;

(2) The presence of two or more alternative forms of a determinant in the cells that initiate and perpetuate the segregation, that is, a heteroplasmic condition;

(3) The irregular distribution of the alternative forms of the determinant at some cell division.

Both cytological observations and breeding experiments show that these conditions are satisfied by many examples of plastid variegation.

	PROPOSED SPORE CONSTITUTIONS							
Frequency of proposed spore constitutions								
OBSERVED	0	1	3	10	7	2	2	0
EXPECTED	0.20	1.37	4.10	6.83	6.83	4.10	1.37	0.20

Fig. 8.2. The frequency with which different spore constitutions, with respect to the relative numbers of mutant to normal homologues of the determinant, are found in a random sample of twenty-five viable asexual spores of the red variant of *Aspergillus*. The spore containing only mutant homologues is presumed to be lethal. (See p. 100.)

Breeding experiments also show that they are fulfilled by the somatically unstable variants of filamentous fungi. The heteroplasmic state is an essential condition for somatic segregation. Let us now consider its origin and the factors affecting its perpetuation.

The origin of heteroplasmons

The heteroplasmic condition may arise in at least two ways (Fig. 8.3). First, it may arise by mutation of some, but not all, homologues of a determinant in a homoplasmic cell. This is analogous to the origin of heterozygosity by a mutation of one allele in a diploid or polyploid chromosome complement, or with the origin of heterokaryosis by a mutation in one nucleus of a multinucleate homokaryotic cell. Second, it may arise by the conjugation of cells with different homoplasmons. This is analogous to the production of heterozygotes by fertilization in a cross between two different homozygotes, or with the production of a heterokaryon by hyphal anastomosis between two different homokaryons (Fig. 8.3). The proof of a heteroplasmic condition like that of heterozygosity or heterokaryosis must rest on the demonstration of segregation due to the sorting out of its components. But to distinguish between a heteroplasmon and a heterocyton (which is defined as a mixture of cells with different homoplasmons), it must be shown that the ability to segregate can be perpetuated through a single cell, whether this be a vegetative cell, an asexual spore, a sexual spore, or a zygote.

In the fungi, there are numerous examples of induced and spontaneous mutations giving rise to a temporary or permanently segregating clone that continues to segregate after propagation by single cells or single spores (see Chapter 5). The degree of persistence of this ability to segregate varies. The least persistent is the so-called unstable state in yeast, which lasts for only a few cell divisions; the most persistent

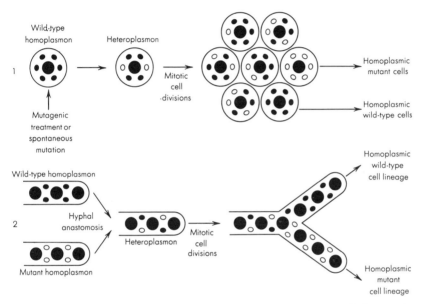

Fig. 8.3. The principal ways in which a heteroplasmic condition may arise: (1) by mutation and (2) by hyphal anastomosis. The heteroplasmon shown in 2 would also occur at fertilization if both parents contributed extrachromosomal material to the zygote and differed in their plasmons. The proof of the heteroplasmic condition lies in its subsequent segregation into its homoplasmic components.

is the red variant of *Aspergillus nidulans*, which continues segregating seven years after its induction. In these instances, the immediate effect of an extrachromosomal mutation is, therefore, to produce a heteroplasmon.

In the fungi, there are also examples of temporary and permanently segregating clones being initiated by the anastomosis of different homoplasmic hyphae, which thereafter can be perpetuated through single cells and spores. For example, the stable *mi* mutants of *Neurospora crassa* will show persistent somatic segregation following hyphal anastomosis with a normal strain. The resulting colony produces hyphae and spores that give rise to further colonies, with phenotypes ranging from mutant to normal through all possible intermediate phenotypes. The hyphae and spores produced by these colonies in many cases repeat this segregation. The hyphal anastomosis has clearly initiated a heteroplasmic state. In the fungi, therefore, there is evidence that the heteroplasmic state arises under the two expected conditions.

In higher plants, the heteroplastid condition has been observed cytologically following both spontaneous and induced plastid mutation. It seems likely that heteroplasmons also arise by the same mechanism. Since cell conjugation normally occurs only at fertilization, when the female gamete contributes most of the extrachromosomal material, this cannot be a general method of heteroplasmon formation. Nevertheless, the heteroplastid condition can arise in this way when there is a male contribution of plastids to the zygote. Hence it seems likely that heteroplasmons may arise occasionally in the same way. The heteroplastid condition subsequently reveals itself by segregating to give a variegated plant.

Stability of heteroplasmons

If the distribution of the alternative forms of a determinant in a heteroplasmic cell is irregular, the heteroplasmon breaks down; it segregates into its component homoplasmons (Fig. 8.1). Furthermore, this breakdown becomes progressively more complete with every round of cell division. If the basic assumptions of the models described earlier hold (see p. 92), the segregants produced by the breakdown of the heteroplasmon should include both homoplasmic components. In addition, the relative frequencies of the two homoplasmic segregants should be equal to the relative frequencies of the alternative forms of the determinant in the original heteroplasmon. In practice, these expectations are rarely realized, for factors that lead to their failure usually prevail.

Suppression

The majority of fungal heteroplasmons, whether they arise by mutation or by the anastomosis of cells with different homoplasmons, sooner or later break down. All the growing tips of the colonies become uniformly homoplasmic for one component of the heteroplasmon. Hence propagations made with these tips give pure breeding colonies that are all like one of the component homoplasmons in phenotype. In general, selection of inocula from regions of the colony that appear to retain the phenotype of the initial heteroplasmon may delay but not prevent the final breakdown. Where the heteroplasmon consists of a mutant and a normal partner, it is usually the gradual loss of the normal component that leads to its breakdown. This is true for heteroplasmons between normal strains and vegetative death, senescence, mycelial, suppressive petite, conidial, *mi*-1, *mi*-3, and *mi*-4, as well as many other variants. Initially, the heteroplasmic colony may have a normal or intermediate phenotype, but gradually it changes to that of its mutant component and all propagation using the growing tips ultimately gives only colonies with the mutant phenotype. At the same time, the proportion of asexual spores that give colonies with a mutant phenotype gradually increases. It is as though the mutant form of the determinant in the heteroplasmon suppressed both the action and the replication of its normal homologues. This situation can be formally accommodated in our model by allowing the a form of the determinant to multiply faster than its normal homologue A.

Insight into a possible mechanism of suppression is available in the case of the poky (mi-1) mutant of *Neurospora crassa*. Herschel K. Mitchell and L. A. Hertzenberg have shown that the mitochondria of poky, in contrast to these from wild type, possess a potent enzyme system that destroys the cytochromes. In vitro, the particles from poky will digest those from wild type, as well as themselves. If this activity also occurs in vivo, it could account for the suppressive action of poky over wild type. In vivo, however, the mitochondria of poky actually accumulate cytochrome c, hence any breakdown must be proceeding very slowly, perhaps too slowly to explain the suppressive effect of poky. Furthermore, F. Sherman and Boris Ephrussi have shown that the suppressive action of petite is independent of its altered biochemical properties. For the present, therefore, suppression is best considered in terms of the superior rate of replication of one form of a determinant over an alternative form, rather than in terms of the destruction of the alternative form.

Suppression in heteroplasmons is in marked contrast to the behavior of mutant and normal genes in the same chromosome complement. Here, the mechanism of division ensures that they are kept in step in reproduction. One cannot replace the other, because they do not compete reproductively. Competition at the extrachromosomal level is presumably another reflection of the absence of comparable reproductive controls during the replication of plasmagenes and the structures that bear them. Perhaps a closer comparison might be expected between a heteroplasmon and the behavior of mutant and normal genes contained in different chromosome sets, as in a heterokaryon. Under these conditions, the mutant and normal genes are free to compete in reproduction. In the majority of reported cases, the two kinds of nuclei achieve equilibrium frequencies compatible with an optimal rate of growth. Optimal growth is often achieved only in those growing tips where the wild-type chromosome set is in the homokaryotic state; when this happens, the heterokaryon breaks down. But it does so in favor of its competitively superior component. In general, this is the wild-type component. There are, however, rare instances of gene mutations that are competitively superior to wild type in heterokaryotic association and that produce homokaryotic mutant sectors, even under conditions where the mutant is lethal in the homokaryotic state. Thus the exceptional behavior at the chromosomal level is almost the rule at the extrachromosomal level.

If we are correct in assuming that when extrachromosomal mutations first arise they often affect only a minority of the determinants (see p. 86), then clearly these would pass unnoticed in a heteroplasmic condition unless they were suppressive. Hence there is an automatic selection for the recognition and isolation of only the suppressive mutants. For this reason alone the high proportion of known suppressive to nonsuppressive mutants should not be regarded as a special property of the extrachromosomal system. On the other hand, the mere existence of suppressive extrachromosomal mutants distinguishes the heteroplasmic from the heterozygous state.

Lethal mutations and permanent heteroplasmons

Heterozygosity in the chromosomal system protects lethal mutations from immediate elimination; such mutations may therefore be detected and analyzed. If we are correct in claiming that heteroplasmons are the extrachromosomal equivalent of heterozygotes, we should expect lethal mutations to be preserved, at least temporarily, in the heteroplasmic state. Does this in fact occur?

The evidence from plastid mutants clearly supports the view that it does. Abnormal plastids that are lethal in the homoplastid plant condition will survive and multiply in the heteroplastid condition, or in plants that are heterocytons. Also, evidence from the fungi indicates that lethal mutants may be retained almost indefinitely in the heteroplasmic state. The red variant of *Aspergillus nidulans* is stable during vegetative growth, but the asexual spores it produces give rise to colonies whose phenotypes vary from wild type to an extreme mutant type. A small but regular proportion of the wild-type colonies are pure-breeding homoplasmic wild types. No corresponding pure-breeding homoplasmic red mutant has been obtained from the original red strain, although consistent selection of the most mutant colonies has been practiced through many propagations. What makes this more remarkable is that the mutant determinants appear to be suppressive. Thus colonies of this variant, whether initially mutant or almost normal in appearance, become uniformly mutant in phenotype as they grow. At the same time, the proportion of their asexual spores, which on germination give rise to colonies with a mutant phenotype, increases steadily from a few per cent to about 70 per cent. Apart from the failure to isolate the pure-breeding mutant homoplasmon, every other property of the red variant is predictable from the assumption that it is a heteroplasmon. It is probable, therefore, that the mutant homoplasmon is lethal.

In addition to the failure to isolate the mutant homoplasmon from the heteroplasmon, there is other evidence, albeit indirect, that the mutant is lethal. For example, the higher the proportion of colonies with a mutant phenotype produced by a sample of asexual spores, the lower the viability of that sample. Furthermore, on aging such samples of spores, those spores that would have given rise to mutant colonies become inviable five times faster than those in the same sample that would have given normal colonies. Asexual spores containing sufficient mutant determinants to give rise to a mutant colony, therefore, are subvital; they have a reduced viability on formation and they degenerate faster on aging. Furthermore, the higher the proportion of mutant segregants produced by a sample of asexual spores (hence, presumably, the higher the frequency of spores containing a high proportion of mutant homologues), the greater is this inviability. There is, therefore, a correlation between the presence and the probable dosage of mutant homologues and inviability. It is reasonable, then, to extrapolate and equate the pure homoplasmic mutant with complete inviability.

If we accept the lethality of the mutant form of the determinant of the red variant, the stability of this variant appears in a new light. The relative frequency of the mutant homologues in the heteroplasmon is continually increasing because of their suppressive action on the wild-type homologues. On the other hand, any cell lineage that contains mainly (or exclusively) mutant determinants will probably die, or at least cease growing. Thus the vegetative stability of the proportions of the mutant and normal forms of the determinant is probably based on a dynamic equilibrium between these two opposing forces.

Vegetative death in *Aspergillus glaucus* is known from direct observation to be both a lethal and a suppressive mutant (see Fig. 6.1). For this mutant, the two opposing forces, lethality and suppression, are not balanced in the heteroplasmic state. It therefore breaks down to give only homoplasmic mutant growing points that show the characteristic properties of vegetative death. All attempts to propagate the colony with them fail. As in the case of the red variant, the asexual spores of these unstable heteroplasmons produce only two classes of colony, the homoplasmic wild type and the heteroplasmon. The former are pure-breeding wild-type colonies, while the latter repeat the behavior just described. The heteroplasmic colonies produce many lethal and sublethal asexual spores. The lethal spores, which are frequently the commonest class produced, cannot be tested further; the spores of the sublethal class, however, can. On germination, the first few hyphae they produce show all the symptoms of vegetative death. Hence they never give rise to a colony that is visible to the naked eye. The lethal and sublethal classes are presumably those spores that are either homoplasmic mutant or predominantly mutant.

These examples show that lethal mutations may be preserved in the heteroplasmic state. Furthermore if, in this state, the mutant determinants are suppressive, the lethal mutant can be detected and many of its properties investigated.

Many alleles, many loci

Chapter 7 explains the conclusion that the extrachromosomal system must have either many alleles or many loci. There is, of course, the further possibility that if many loci are involved they may be borne on the same or on different extrachromosomal structures. That is, they may be physically linked or unlinked. The method of distinguishing these three levels is a commonplace of chromosomal heredity. To what extent can the criteria and tests used in chromosomal heredity be adapted to draw similar distinctions at the extrachromosomal level?

Functional test

In the extrachromosomal system, the distinction between two mutations at the same site and at two different sites on the same physical structure must rest largely on functional comparisons. The additional criterion available at the chromosomal level, namely, recombination, can hardly be regarded as a practical test at the present time. If, therefore, the two mutants affect the same function, we must conclude for the time being that they occupy the same site. On the other hand, if they are functionally independent, we may conclude that they occupy different sites. The functional test, however, does not tell us whether the different sites are on the same or a different extrachromosomal structure.

In practice, the functional test requires only that the phenotype of a heteroplasmon between the two mutants under investigation be de-

Fig. 8.4. A functional test to distinguish mutations at the same or at functionally different sites on an extrachromosomal structure. One such structure is shown bearing two functional units. Mutants 1 and 2 affect the same function, but mutant 3 affects a different function.

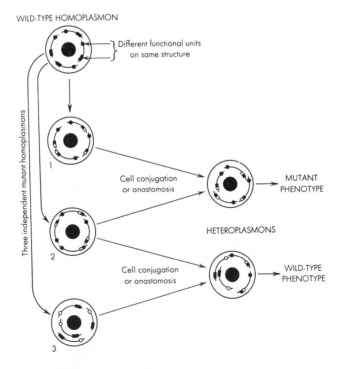

termined. If the two mutants affect the same function, the heteroplasmon will itself be defective for the same function, and hence it will be mutant in phenotype. If they affect different functions, each mutant homoplasmon will contribute the wild-type function that is lacking in its partner. We expect, therefore, some measure of compensation or complementation; the heteroplasmon should have a wild phenotype, or, at least, a phenotype that is more nearly wild type than the phenotype of either mutant homoplasmon (Fig. 8.4).

Segregational test

To distinguish between different sites on the same physical structure and sites on independent structures, we must determine whether the sites show linked or independent transmission. If two mutants occupy different sites on the same structure, then in a heteroplasmon between them the two mutants will segregate as strict alternatives at the determinant level. But since each cell will probably contain many representatives of the determinant, they will not be strict alternatives at the cell level. Indeed, many cells will be heteroplasmic. Nevertheless, homoplasmic cells, as sectors and spores that are pure for one or another component, will ultimately arise by somatic segregation (Fig. 8.5).

Fig. 8.5. A segregation test to distinguish mutations on the same and on different extrachromosomal structures. Mutants 1 and 2 occupy different sites on the same structure, and mutant 3 occupies a site on a different structure.

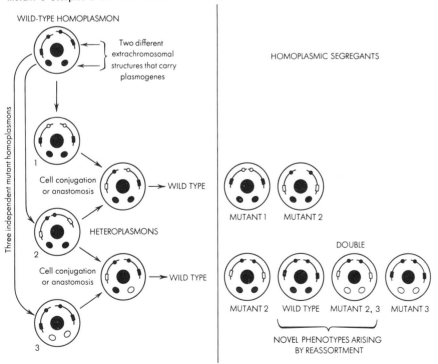

If the two mutants occupy sites on different, nonhomologous structures, then each mutant homoplasmon will contain the normal homologue of the other mutant. In the heteroplasmic state, therefore, we should expect complementation and also reassortment to produce cell lineages that are permanently wild-type because they contain only the wild-type homologues brought into the heteroplasmon by the two mutants. In addition, we should expect the reciprocal product of reassortment, namely, cells containing only the mutant form of both determinants, that is, the double mutant. In practice it would be necessary to distinguish between a wild phenotype, resulting from complementation between two mutants, and one resulting from reassortment, giving a wild-type homoplasmon. This would require a simple breeding test; the wild-type heteroplasmon would continue to show somatic segregation; the wild-type homoplasmon would have irreversibly lost the capacity to do so. Thus the distinction between mutants occupying sites on the same and on different structures must rest, ultimately, on the nonrecovery or recovery of a pure-breeding wild-type homoplasmon from a double heteroplasmon, respectively (Fig. 8.5).

The possibility of recombination between different sites on the same extrachromosomal structure has so far been ignored. We have no evidence that it occurs. But if it does, wild-type homoplasmons could arise from a heteroplasmon, irrespective of whether the two mutants occupied sites on the same structure or on different structures. Nevertheless, mutants at unlinked sites would be expected to produce a higher frequency of wild-type homoplasmic segregants than mutants at linked sites. This simple model, however, ignores the complications introduced by suppression, and hence the loss of components from the heteroplasmic association. Such complications make meaningful quantitative predictions impossible. The segregational test must be regarded, therefore, as a qualitative test, without the ability to distinguish between recombination of linked sites and reassortment of unlinked sites.

In this discussion, nonhomologous extrachromosomal structures that bear plasmagenes have been likened to linkage groups. The test for detecting extrachromosomal linkage depends on the validity of this analogy. In making it, we assume that nonhomologous extrachromosomal structures segregate at random, relative to one another, to the two daughter cells, as do nonhomologous chromosomes at meiosis. For example, if a structure I is heteroplasmic at a site Aa and a structure II is heteroplasmic at a site Bb, the assumption is that their irregular distribution at cell division will produce four classes of homoplasmic segregants, $IAIIB$, $IAIIb$, $IaIIB$, and $IaIIb$. Since we are not concerned with exact quantitative expectations, deviations from randomness are not important so long as all four classes are produced. Furthermore, since the segregation of alternative forms of a single determinant Aa is in some cases almost random (see pp. 92-93), it seems probable that two alternative forms of two different unlinked determinants might behave similarly with respect to one another.

Application of tests to mi variants

The only systematic examination of the relationships between independently occurring extrachromosomal mutants was carried out by Thad H. Pittenger and Barbara Gowdridge, using the *mi* series of mutants of *Neurospora crassa*. Both have independently described the properties of the poky/*mi*-3 heteroplasmon, and Pittenger has investigated in detail the more interesting poky/*mi*-4 heteroplasmon. The poky/*mi*-3 combination had a mutant phenotype, and the growth habit resembled one or the other mutant component on different occasions. The poky/*mi*-4 combination, on the other hand, had the growth rate of a wild-type strain for about the first 1,000 millimeters of growth, although spectroscopic analysis showed that the cytochrome system was as abnormal as in the mutants. Thus while poky and *mi*-4 can compensate for each other's deficiencies in rate of growth, they cannot jointly produce a normal respiratory enzyme system. Because, presumably, of its superior rate of growth, the heteroplasmon has some measure of stability. Sooner or later, however, it becomes mutant in phenotype. We can only assume that this breakdown is the result of the suppressive action of one or both of its mutant components. From this functional test, we must conclude that poky and *mi*-3 are functionally identical and hence they are allelic (see mutants 1 and 2, Fig. 8.4) and that poky and *mi*-4 are functionally independent, at least in part, and hence they occupy different loci (see mutants 2 and 3, Fig. 8.4).

The segregational behavior of the heteroplasmons suggests that all three mutants are alleles of loci borne on the same extrachromosomal structure. Poky and *mi*-3 behaved almost as though they were mutually exclusive, and growing tips from the heteroplasmon gave colonies that behaved like one or another homoplasmon. Poky and *mi*-4 could be recovered from the heteroplasmon as a result of somatic segregation during asexual spore formation and branching. In addition, various intermediates were also recovered. These were unstable and behaved as though they were different quantitative mixtures of the two mutants. Neither heteroplasmon gave a stable homoplasmon that differed from either component homoplasmon. There is, therefore, no evidence of reassortment or recombination. Hence our tentative conclusion is that poky and *mi*-3 occupy one site, and *mi*-4 a different site on the same extrachromosomal structure (Fig. 8.4).

Apart from a few inconclusive experiments with *Aspergillus*, these results from *Neurospora* stand alone; they nevertheless show that functional and segregational criteria of the kind used to distinguish alleles, loci, and linkage groups at the chromosomal level can be adapted to investigate the nature of the extrachromosomal system.

They also show that these familiar levels of organization can probably be defined and recognized in the extrachromosomal system.

Uniparental transmission

The properties of the extrachromosomal system related to its ability to segregate at somatic cell divisions are probably the most characteristic of all the properties of the system, and it seems likely that many of the remaining problems will be solved by study of them. In sexual reproduction, however, there is found an equally characteristic property of the system, namely, maternal or uniparental inheritance. The usual and trivial explanation of maternal transmission is that the larger female gamete contains determinants that are excluded from or present in reduced numbers in the smaller male gamete. Breeding experiments (see Chapters 2, 3, and 4) show that uniparental transmission occurs in algae such as *Chlamydomonas reinhardi,* where the whole organism is the gamete and the zygote is produced by the fusion of equal gametes (see Fig. 4.1). Since both parents contribute all their substance to the zygote, the nontransmission of the plasmagenes contributed by one parent must imply postconjugational destruction of its contribution. Cytological observations of the algae *Zygnema* and *Rhynchonema* (see Chapter 2) have shown that the plastids contributed by one parent to the zygote are regularly eliminated, or rather destroyed, after conjugation. This action provides a visible model of what may be happening to other extrachromosomal bearers of plasmagenes. In these two species, all the contents of a single cell are contributed to the zygote by both parents, but the plastids contributed by the more active parent, the "male," are subsequently destroyed, leaving only the female contribution to be inherited by the progeny. This type of behavior is by no means confined to algae. In the gymnosperm *Pinus*, the cytoplasmic granular material, including mitochondria and proplastids, contributed by the male disintegrates after first congregating in one region of the fertilized oosphere that contributes nothing to the embryo.

In view of these kinds of observation, it is difficult to avoid the conclusion that maternal inheritance involves a more fundamental mechanism than the mere inability of the smaller male gametes to carry the plasmagenes. Uniparental transmission predates the evolution of smaller male gametes. If the smaller size of the male gamete plays any part in this process, it is secondary and dependent on the fact that uniparental transmission is already an established system. If the small size of the male gamete is not the primary cause, what is?

Compensatory reduction
of extrachromosomal complement

At the chromosome level, the doubling of the complement that occurs at fertilization is counterbalanced by a reduction division, meiosis, which halves it once more. In the lower plants, where the number of chloroplasts per cell is small and constant, the chloroplasts divide in step with the chromosome complement at each cell division. Fertilization, therefore, would double the number of chloroplasts at the same time that it doubles the chromosome complement. But there is no reduction division to halve the number of chloroplasts again. Nevertheless, a variety of ways of reducing the chloroplast complement has evolved (Fig. 8.6). In *Chlamydomonas, Zygnema,* and *Rhyncho-*

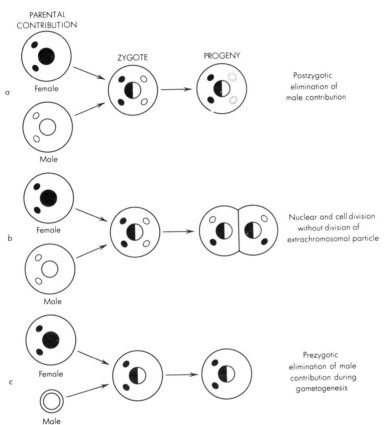

Fig. 8.6. Three methods of achieving a constant balance between chromosomal and extra-chromosomal hereditary material from one generation to the next. All three are found in the lower plants and occasionally in the higher plants. Method c, however, is the commonest of the three.

nema, the contribution of one parent shows postzygotic destruction; in the alga *Vaucheria* and the liverwort *Anthoceros,* there is prezygotic elimination of plastids during the genesis of the male gametes but they are retained in the female gamete; and in *Coleochaete,* there is one division of the chromosome complement during meiosis without a corresponding division of the zygotic complement of chloroplasts, which is thereby halved. All achieve the same end, but only the method found in *Vaucheria* and *Anthoceros* allows any reduction in the size of the more active gamete. And this is the method most commonly found in higher plants, where a smaller male gamete is the rule. Nevertheless, it is by no means the only method found, even among the flowering plants. Male transmission occurs in some species with the same frequency as female transmission. We can only assume that in such species postzygotic or prezygotic reduction affects both parental contributions equally.

Uniparental transmission of the plastids and perhaps of other extrachromosomal components is in one sense the equivalent of the reduction division of the chromosome complement. Whether this reduction is achieved by prezygotic elimination or postzygotic destruction is immaterial to this analogy. Which sex suffers the elimination depends on the nature of the structures involved, as does also the timing of the elimination. Centrioles, which are associated with the production of the sperm tail, play an essential role in spermatogenesis; it is not surprising, therefore, that there is no prezygotic elimination of centrioles in the male gametes. Similarly, they are essential in oogenesis up to the end of the second meiotic division, which gives the chromosome complement of the egg, hence they cannot be eliminated before this stage. Since prezygotic elimination is impossible, only two methods of reduction remain, a division of the chromosome complement of the zygote without a corresponding division of the centrioles (Fig. 8.6b) or the postzygotic destruction of one pair of centrioles (Fig. 8.6a). In amphibian zygotes, it is claimed that the reduction is achieved by the failure of the female centrioles to function after fertilization. (See Chapter 2.) As a consequence, all the centrioles of the developing embryo are paternal in origin.

Viewed as a reduction mechanism, uniparental transmission brings together the apparently opposing maternal and paternal inheritance of extrachromosomal bodies. Whether or not this is the correct interpretation, it must be clear from the evidence discussed that there is more to uniparental transmission than the difference in size of the uniting gametes. Indeed, if the interpretation is correct the latter is a consequence rather than a cause.

Conclusions

In their replication and distribution at cell divisions, some extrachromosomal entities are as regular as chromosomes. Others are irregular; the result is that segregation may occur for extrachromosomally inherited differences at mitotic cell divisions. The simplest model of the extrachromosomal system that will account for persistent segregation at cell divisions must possess three properties.

(1) It must have more than one homologue of the determinant per cell.

(2) The cell that initiates and perpetuates the segregation must be heteroplasmic.

(3) A proportion of the cells must have irregular distribution of the alternative forms of the determinant when they divide.

Such a model, also assuming that the alternative forms of the determinant are distributed at random at cell divisions, fits examples of plastid segregations in *Epilobium* and persistently segregating variants of *Aspergillus*.

There are two known causes of the failure of the simple model to explain particular examples of segregation.

(1) Suppression: one form of a determinant in its action and replication is superior to its alternative in the heteroplasmon. The superior component is frequently a mutant form.

(2) Lethality of the mutant of a determinant: segregants that contain mainly (or exclusively) the mutant form of the determinant are lethal. The heteroplasmic state preserves such mutants.

In chromosomal heredity, functional and segregational tests are used to subdivide the hereditary material into linkage groups, loci, and alleles. The same tests applied, as far as we are able to apply them, to the extrachromosomal system recognize similar subdivisions.

Although segregation at mitotic cell divisions is characteristic of some extrachromosomally inherited differences, uniparental inheritance at sexual reproduction is equally characteristic of others. Uniparental inheritance, whether maternal or paternal, is understandable in terms of a compensating reducing mechanism for the doubling of the extrachromosomal complement that would otherwise occur at fertilization.

References

Jinks, John L., "Cytoplasmic Inheritance in Fungi," in *Methodology in Basic Genetics*, W. J. Burdette, ed. (San Francisco: Holden-Day, Inc., 1963).

Michaelis, Peter, "Genetische, entwicklungsgeschichtliche, und zytologische Untersuchungen zur Plasmavererbung, I," *Flora (Jena), 151* (1961), 162.

Sager, Ruth, and Y. Tsubo, "Genetic Analysis of Streptomycin Resistance and Dependence in Chlamydomonas," *Z. Vererbungslehre, 92* (1961), 430.

Questions

8.1. Why is it necessary to assume that the determinants of extrachromosomal heredity frequently show irregular segregation at mitotic cell divisions?

8.2. Compare and contrast the properties of the heterozygous and the heteroplasmic states.

8.3. Cytologically we can distinguish three methods for reducing the extrachromosomal complement at fertilization. What are their consequences for traits that are extrachromosomally determined?

8.4. The heteroplasmon between two mutant strains of a fungus gives a wild-type growth. What does this observation tell us about the relationship between the two mutants? Suggest further tests for clarifying this relationship.

Hereditary Symbiosis

It is often claimed that the determinants of extra-chromosomal heredity are viruses. It is also claimed with equal confidence that the constituents of a normal cell may exhibit viral properties if circumstances change. To support such contrary claims, there must clearly be considerable overlap in the properties of viruses and hereditary determinants.

Properties of determinants

An examination of this overlap, particularly where it concerns extrachromosomal determinants, is essential for an analysis of the extrachromosomal system. At the same time, we must consider how far extrachromosomally situated viruses and similar intracellular organisms may be regarded as markers for following the behavior of extrachromosomal cell constituents in heredity, and hence the additional light their study throws on the mechanism of extrachromosomal heredity. We must also consider to what extent the transmission of these intracellular organisms from one cell generation to another constitutes a special case of extrachromosomal transmission of hereditary information. Let us begin by looking at three cases of extrachromosomal inheritance where the determinant is claimed to be a virus or a similar foreign body.

Killer trait

The first example concerns the so-called killer trait in *Paramecium aurelia*, variety 2. Tracy M. Sonneborn's elucidation of its inheritance in the early 1940's was one of the most significant events in the study of extrachromosomal heredity. He discovered that certain strains of *P. aurelia* produce and liberate into the surrounding medium a substance called paramecin, which kills some strains but never the producers. The producers are known as killers, and the strains that they kill are known as sensitives. To be a killer, a strain must contain kappa particles in its cytoplasm. (A kappa is a minute particle about 0.4 microns long. It possesses its own DNA, and J. R. Preer has likened it to a *Rickettsia* virus in its general appearance.) To keep the kappa particles in its cytoplasm, the strain must carry one dominant gene at the K, S_1, S_2, and possibly at other chromosomal loci.

Before kappa particles had even been seen, their presence had been postulated and their frequency estimated by breeding experiments (Fig. 9.1). Sonneborn conjugated killer animals of stock 51 and sensitives of stock 52 and found that from each pair the two exconjugants produced different clones; those clones that had derived their extrachromosomal material from the killer parent were killers, and those that derived it from the sensitive parent were sensitive. Both exconjugants, of course, had identical chromosomal complements (see Figs. 3.1 and 3.2). Under normal conditions, there is no substantial transfer of extrachromosomal material between parental cells of these stocks during conjugation. However, in crosses between stock 51 killers and stock 47 sensitives, the cytoplasmic bridge between conjugants may persist after the completion of normal conjugation, and under these circumstances both exconjugants produce killer animals. If the bridge persists for only a short period, the sensitive exconjugant sometimes yields a sensitive clone and sometimes a killer clone. These results, which are similar in all respects to those obtained with mating type and serotype differences (see Chapters 4 and 6), indicate the presence of an extrachromosomally transmitted factor in the killer cells that determines their killer trait.

A killer may be transformed into a sensitive by many treatments that are now known to lead to the loss of the extrachromosomal factor, kappa. These include exposure to high temperatures, X rays, nitrogen mustard, and chloromycetin. By crossing sensitives derived in this way with killers, it can be shown that the difference resides solely in their extrachromosomal content (Fig. 9.1).

When sensitive cells that have lost their kappa particles but that possess the chromosomal genes K, S_1, and S_2 are placed in concentrated suspensions of disintegrated killer animals, some are converted into killers; that is, they acquire kappa from the suspension. Hence the extrachromosomal factor of the killer trait is infectious.

Kappa is subject to mutation, and mutant forms differ in the amount and kind of paramecin they produce. One animal can carry two forms of kappa; the result is a condition equivalent to a heteroplasmon. Thus kappa has all the essential properties of an extrachromosomal particle possessing genetic continuity. Indeed, apart from its in vitro infectivity, its characteristics are shared by plastids and other postu-

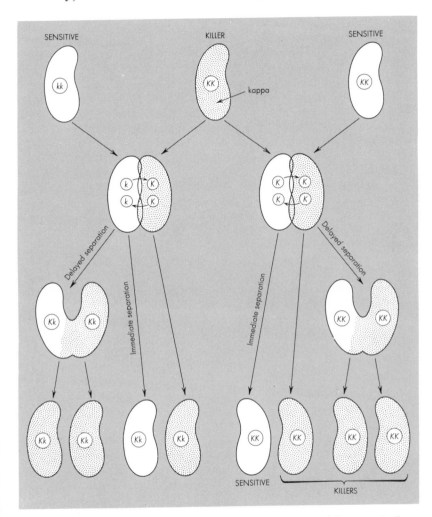

Fig. 9.1. Inheritance of the killer trait in *Paramecium aurelia*. To be a killer, an animal must contain kappa particles and a number of dominant genes of which one, *K*, is shown. For further details see Figs. 3.1, 3.2, 3.3, and 6.3. Based on Tracy M. Sonneborn, "Gene and Cytoplasm I and II," *Proc. Nat. Acad. Sci. U.S.,* 29 (1943).

lated, but as yet unseen, determinants of extrachromosomal heredity. What, therefore, are the grounds on which kappa is classified as a foreign intracellular organism? First, kappa particles are not present in most paramecia; therefore, they are hardly a normal extrachromosomal component, nor can they be of great importance in the hereditary make-up of most paramecia. The same argument could be used in relation to the chloroplasts of *Euglena*. On the other hand, while kappa is limited in its distribution, it is only one of a large class of cytoplasmic bodies found in *Paramecium,* some of which have obvious homologies with kappa itself. Second, the presence of DNA in kappa distinguishes it from most of the particles commonly found in the cytoplasm of cells, although it now seems likely that it shares this property with plastids (see Chapter 7). Third, its ability to mutate has been cited in favor of kappa as an independent organism, but it must be apparent that this ability is shared by every example of extrachromosomal heredity that has been described. Hence, if there is a difference between kappa and plastids or any postulated extrachromosomal determinant, it is one of degree and not one of kind.

CO_2 sensitivity

The second example concerns the inheritance of CO_2 sensitivity in *Drosophila melanogaster.* P. H. l'Heritier and G. Tessier discovered strains of *D. melanogaster* that, unlike normal strains, were abnormally sensitive to atmospheres rich in CO_2. After exposure to such atmospheres, these sensitive strains died. L'Heritier and his colleagues have interpreted this sensitivity in terms of a hypothetical cytoplasmic particle, sigma. The F_1 from a cross between a pure-breeding sensitive female and a resistant male is always sensitive, and behaves in further repeated backcrosses to resistant males like the sensitive strains. The reciprocal cross between a resistant female and a sensitive male always gives both resistant and sensitive offspring, but in varying and obviously non-Mendelian proportions. The mode of inheritance is clearly extrachromosomal. This has been proved by replacing all the chromosomes of a sensitive strain by those of a resistant strain, using the special breeding techniques available in *D. melanogaster,* without affecting its sensitivity.

The postulated extrachromosomal particle sigma, whose presence causes sensitivity, is infective, in the sense that resistant flies may be transformed to sensitives by implanting pieces of organs or extracts of a sensitive fly into a resistant fly. Sensitivity acquired in this way behaves, at least initially, somewhat differently from the usual sensitive strains. For example, females with newly acquired sensitivity transmit it to some of their off-spring but similar males transmit it to none. Thus while some oocytes become infected in the female, the sperms of the male do not. Nevertheless, any sensitives in the progeny of these crosses breed like typical sensitives in subsequent generations.

The persistence, and hence, presumably, the multiplication of sigma, is not dependent on any specific chromosomal gene; indeed, it can be transmitted successfully to a number of different species of *Drosophila.* It is, however, sensitive to environmental conditions, particularly temperature. Temperatures of 30°C. or above convert sensitives to resistants by inactivating or destroying sigma.

Sigma may mutate. One variant form, referred to as omega, differs in that it is rarely male-transmitted. A second mutant, iota, confers some measure of resistance to infection by sigma, but it is not itself infectious. The most interesting condition is rho, in which flies are resistant to CO_2 until a certain age, when they become sensitive. While resistant, they yield no infective agent, but they are immune to infection. When they become sensitive, they produce an infective agent that is indistinguishable from sigma.

None of these particles has yet been seen nor has their chemical nature yet been analyzed, but they are remarkably similar to kappa in their mode of inheritance, infectivity, and mutability, and like kappa there is little to distinguish sigma from any other postulated extrachromosomally inherited particle. The argument for its viral nature, in fact, rests on its over-all similarity to proviruses in bacteria. This similarity will become apparent when the latter system is described later in this chapter.

"Sex ratio"

Our third example is the inheritance of the condition known as sex ratio (SR), which has been worked out in *Drosophila willistoni* primarily by C. Malogolowkin and D. F. Poulson. SR strains produce progenies that are predominantly or exclusively female. The rarity or absence of males is a consequence of their mortality during embryonic development. Occasionally, a son of an SR female survives, and reciprocal crosses between SR and normal strains can be made. These show that the SR condition is transmitted only through the female gamete.

The agent responsible for the death of the embryonic males can be extracted, and when introduced into females of a normal strain it infectively transforms them to the SR condition. The infective agent can also be isolated from various tissues, particularly the haemolymph of mature, adult females of the SR strains. In *D. willistoni* it is now known that the infective agent is a spirachaete, whose presence can be demonstrated by electron micrographs of infected tissues. The SR condition is also known in *D. bifasciata, D. prosaltans,* and *D. equinoxialis,* and it can be infectively transferred between the last named and *D. willistoni.* Thus the casual agent, like sigma, is relatively insensitive to the chromosomal gene complement with which it is associated. It also shares with sigma a sensitivity to high temperatures, which by inactivating or destroying it produce strains that are "cured" of their SR condition.

To summarize: the inheritance of the killer trait, CO_2 sensitivity, and SR satisfy the criteria of extrachromosomal heredity, and two of them, the killer trait and SR, are invariably associated with cytologically demonstrable particles that satisfy the criteria for genetic continuity. All three are due to infective agents that are transmissible by artificial means. Two of the infective agents, kappa and the spirachaete of SR, are almost certainly extraneous in origin. But on the breeding experiments alone, there is nothing that clearly distinguishes them from normal extrachromosomal cell constituents that are known, or believed, to carry hereditary information. The possibility arises, therefore, that the killer trait and SR are not alone among extrachromosomally inherited traits in being determined in this way. Are there, in fact, other examples of extrachromosomal heredity whose properties are so like those of the killer trait and SR that it seems likely that their determinants are also extraneous in origin?

Essential and nonessential symbionts

Neither kappa nor the SR agent is essential for normal cell metabolism or for cell reproduction; either may be lost without harm, or even with beneficial results. The difference between the variant and the alternative conditions is in both cases due to the presence and absence, respectively, of the extrachromosomal particle. Both conditions are infective, but hereditary transmission is the most effective and the only established method of natural spread.

The plastids of organism such as *Euglena* share the first of these properties; they or their function may be lost without killing the organism, and in nature, races and species of *Euglena* exist that possess no plastids. In this respect, the plastids of *Euglena* are like the algal symbionts of *Paramecium* species and lichens, in that they can be lost without killing the host. It would be nonsense, however, to suggest that no benefit results from the photosynthetic activity of either the plastids or the algal symbionts. Indeed, an autotrophic existence is totally dependent on their presence. In these circumstances, it is advantageous for the association to persist throughout vegetative life, and to be perpetuated into the next generation.

In unicellular organisms, intracellular ingestion of foreign organisms is a preliminary to digestion; furthermore, the same cell is at different times the soma and the gamete. The origin and perpetuation of intracellular associations, therefore, presents no special difficulties. Hence in this group, which includes both *Euglena* and *Paramecium*, we should not be surprised to find that the hereditary transmission of symbionts and parasites is commonplace. *Euglena*, *Paramecium*, and the fungal components of lichens are all capable of an independent, heterotrophic existence; the loss of the plastids or the plastid bearers is not lethal. This is not true, however, of the algal components; the loss of their plastids or of plastid functions is as lethal as it is in all autotrophic plants. Thus the plastids of *Euglena* and the algal symbionts of ciliates and lichens may be equated with kappa or the agent of SR. They are all dispensable. But they cannot be equated, on this criterion, with the plastids of autotrophic plants. The argument, which has been made by some researchers, that the ancestors of the plastids of autotrophic plants were symbiotic or parasitic algal-like organisms does not alter the fact that the plastids no longer behave as such. They are now transmitted solely by heredity as indispensable extrachromosomal cell constituents. Acceptance of the extraneous origin of plastids in no way alters the interpretation of the inheritance of plastid differences in present-day autotrophic plants.

Active and passive infection

Infection with sigma, the agent of SR, and with kappa, across the conjugation bridge, has its counterpart in the infective heredity of some of the extrachromosomal mutants of fungi (see Chapter 6). Kappa, however, can infect in vitro, and, although it does so with a very low frequency and probably passively, this ability is a distinctive property that has not been demonstrated for any other extrachromosomally inherited particle. But is this a real distinction? In vitro infection of *Paramecium* with kappa or even an algal symbiont can be achieved by the crudest techniques, presumably, because they passively enter by the gullet, and all that is required of the infector is that it should escape digestion. If plastids could be kept in a fully functional condition in vitro, there is no reason why a plastid-free strain of *Euglena* could not be infected by the same mechanism. Much more, however, would be involved in infecting a fungus or a higher plant with a cell-free isolate of an extrachromosomal particle. The isolate would first have to be extracted and probably purified in an active state, and maintained in this state until such time as attempts could be made to introduce it into another cell. No method exists for ingesting macromolecules, let alone structures the size of plastids, in an intact condition in either the fungi or the higher plants. We can be certain, therefore, that merely growing these plants in a suspension of the particles would not result in infection. There is no reason to doubt that the technical problem of introducing them by mechanical injection could be solved. It is difficult to see, however, what could be concluded about the infectivity of the particles under these circumstances that is not already apparent from the results of hyphal anastomosis in fungi. Certainly a mechanical transfer of a purified extrachromosomal particle from one cell to another, if successful, could provide an elegant proof of the genetic continuity of a mutant particle, but it does not help us to resolve the difference, if any, between infection by migration across a cytoplasmic bridge and infection by ingestion through a gullet.

Neither of these is the type of behavior associated with viral infection. Viruses usually take an active part in their dispersal and entry into a host cell and their dispersal is often mediated by an active vector. On the other hand, some conditions that have been ascribed to viruses show only passive transmission. For example, the latent virus of the King Edward potato can only be transmitted by injection or by grafting it onto another potato variety; this passive property it shares with kappa, sigma, the agent of SR, and the infective extrachromosomal mutants of fungi. But what are we to conclude? That the ability to infect by this means is a common property of both viruses and plasmagenes? That the King Edward latent virus is a plasmagene? Or that the infective extrachromosomal mutants are viruses? Cyril D. Darlington has argued that the nearest distinction that can be made between plasmagenes and viruses is that plasmagenes are transmitted and viruses are not transmitted through the germ cells in sexual reproduction. On this basis, kappa, sigma, SR, and those infective extrachromosomal mutants that are sexually fertile are demonstrably plasmagenes. But, as Darlington is the first to admit, this distinction, although generally valid, does break down. We can only conclude, therefore, that the kind of infectivity exhibited by kappa, sigma, and SR is not particularly helpful in discriminating between plasmagenes and viral particles. Indeed, for this property there is no real distinction between these three and the infective fungal variants.

Normal cell constituent or virus

An extrachromosomal mutant is, in general, the result of an alteration in a particle or plasmagene of a normal cell, rather than the absence of such a particle (see Chapter 7). Furthermore, the presence of the normal particle or plasmagene is often critical, and the loss of its function lethal. The phenotypic change produced by a viral infection, on the other hand, is due to the presence of a particle that is not a normal constituent of a cell, and hence has no counterpart or homologue in a normal cell. The distinction between a wild-type cell and an abnormal cell in this case depends on the absence and presence of a particle, respectively. Thus at the determinant level there is no problem in defining the difference between an extrachromosomal variant and a virus. But can this definition be used in practice to distinguish the two?

Where the particle involved is visible, this distinction can be made. For example, cytological observations show that most wild-type paramecia lack kappa particles, and most wild-type drosophilae lack the agent of SR. In contrast, the plastid mutants of obligate autotrophs contain abnormal homologues of those present in wild-type cells. Where the particles are not visible, the only prospect of distinguishing kappa, SR, and normal extrachromosomal cell constituents that possess genetic continuity is on the basis of their mutability. Kappa can mutate to give different types of killer, and it can also be lost to give sensitives. But sensitives cannot mutate to give killers; they cannot regain the lost genetic information contained in kappa except by reinfection.

Extrachromosomal mutants, insofar as they are the result of an alteration in a particle or plasmagene of a normal cell, are capable of backmutation; they retain the genetic continuity. Hence both the wild type and the mutant are capable of giving rise to the alternative form by mutation and backmutation, respectively. In theory, at least, mutability studies could provide the basis of a classification of plasmagenes and viral agents. Unfortunately, as we have already had reason to note in Chapter 7, backmutation studies on extrachromosomally inherited mutants are almost nonexistent; we cannot, therefore, assess the usefulness of this criterion.

The mutability test is, in fact, a restatement of an earlier conclusion, namely, that supernumerary particles such as kappa may suffer a "mutation" involving their physical elimination, while essential constituents of normal cells may not. Even this statement has its exceptions, for a normal cell constituent of one variety or species may be a supernumerary when introduced into another species. If the supernumerary, however, takes on viral properties in its new cell environment, then it ceases to be an exception. The latent virus of King Edward potatoes could be regarded in this light, for an apparently normal cell constituent of this variety behaves as a virus when introduced into other varieties. Nor is this example unique. A cell constituent of *Beta maritima* seedlings, when injected into plants of *Vigna sinesis*, multiplies in the new host and generates an infectious viral agent. In both cases, the virus is a normal cell constituent of the donor, for all King Edward potatoes and all seedlings of *B. maritima* at a particular stage of development possess them. They are also supernumerary to the normal cell complement of the hosts into which they are introduced. Looked at in this way, a plasmagene of the donor becomes a virus in the recipient.

Looked at in a different way, the King Edward latent virus, while common to all potatoes of this variety, is not common to all potatoes. It is not, therefore, a normal cell constituent of all potatoes. It is a supernumerary confined to one variety, a virus to which King Edward is tolerant. But let us suppose that this latent virus and the cell constituent of *B. maritima* have homologous cell constituents in the recipients. The so-called viruses produced in the recipient cells are then merely suppressive plasmagenes that oust their homologues from the heteroplasmon that is produced by the injection of the foreign cell contents. While this may not be the correct interpretation of these particular examples, we must admit the possibility that there are particles that develop viral properties under conditions that do not generally occur or that have not previously occurred in nature. To such particles Darlington has given the name *provirus*. Once we admit their existence, attempts to distinguish plasmagene and virus lose much of their meaning. The same entity could be classified as both, according to circumstances, on any criterion that has been devised.

Viral models

Irrespective of our attitude toward the nature of kappa, sigma, and SR, they are undeniably extrachromosomal particles so far as their geographical distribution within the cell is concerned. As Boris Ephrussi first pointed out, they can therefore be regarded as extrachromosomal markers and they can be followed by cytological observations and breeding tests. For this purpose, their biological significance need be no more than that of radioactive tracers or vital stains; they merely mark a region of the cell whose fate we wish to follow.

What do these markers tell us about the various tests and criteria used to detect the extrachromosomal basis of a difference in phenotype?

(1) Persistent matroclinal inheritance occurs when the extrachromosomal determinant, for example, kappa and SR, is transmitted mainly by the maternal parent.

(2) A low frequency of male transmission of SR leads to somatic segregation and non-Mendelian segregations.

(3) The presence of many homologues of a particle, for example, kappa, per cell leads to the origin of a heteroplasmic state by mutation of some homologues or by conjugation of cells containing different forms of the homologue.

(4) When the number of homologues per cell is high (a few hundred for kappa), cells heteroplasmic for different forms of kappa only segregate very slowly into their homoplasmic components.

(5) Heteroplasmons for different forms of kappa break down preferentially to give one homoplasmic component, which is presumably suppressive.

(6) Infective heredity occurs if mobile extrachromosomal material is exchanged between cells with different extrachromosomal complements.

Clearly they confirm the validity of most of the tests that have been used to detect extrachromosomal inheritance.

In one sense, the existence of kappa, sigma, and SR has weakened the case for normal extrachromosomal cell constituents that possess genetic continuity. They lend credence to the view that all such particles are extraneous in origin and viral in nature. In another sense, kappa, sigma, and SR immeasurably strengthen the evidence for the existence of normal cell constituents that possess genetic continuity. They are undeniably extrachromosomal bodies and our breeding tests unambiguously define them as such. We can confidently claim, therefore, that our breeding tests can detect genetic information that is located outside the chromosomal complement, and hence that the deductions we have made from such tests are essentially correct.

Episomes

So far, it has been implied that extrachromosomal material possessing genetic continuity can only arise in three ways: (1) by replication of pre-existing extrachromosomal material in the same cell; (2) by infection with pre-existing extrachromosomal material from a different cell; (3) by infection with an intracellular organism that is extraneous in origin. There is, however, a fourth possibility.

A new type of genetic particle, the episome, has recently been postulated. Its proposers suggest that the episome fills the no man's land between heredity and infection, and between chromosomal and extrachromosomal heredity. In the following discussion the episome is considered from the point of view of a possible fourth way in which extrachromosomally sited genetic information could arise, a way that would account for the origin of sigma; the more formal aspects of episomes are dealt with by Stahl in *The Mechanics of Inheritance*, in this series.

Lysogeny

The concept of the episome was developed in the 1950's from the study of lysogeny in *Escherichia coli* by François Jacob and E. L. Wollman. They showed that a particle possessing genetic continuity, such as the genetic material of a bacteriophage, can anchor itself to the host bacterial chromosome and from then on behave as a chromosomal constituent of the host. In the attached state it corresponds to Darlington's provirus: its viral properties are potential; in the detached state it is a virus. The genetic material of a virus, the so-called temperate virus, that is capable of forming this attachment may exist in one of two states within the host cell, in the extrachromosomal or vegetative state in which it replicates at its own rate as an autonomous unit, or in the chromosomal or provirus state in which it replicates as part of the chromosomal complement. For some time, this alternative state remained a unique feature of temperate viruses, but similar situations have been suggested for other nonviral genetic particles. Nevertheless, whether viral or not, all episomes possess the common property of being inessential constituents of the cell.

When a temperate virus infects a sensitive bacterial cell, only the genetic material of the virus, composed largely or solely of DNA, enters the cell (Fig. 9.2). Upon entry, it may go into the extrachromosomal phase, in which its genetic material replicates much faster than the bacterial genome. At the same time, the protein components of the infective particle are synthesized. Alternatively, the genetic material may enter the chromosomal phase, in which it becomes tied to the bacterial chromosome in such a way that both replicate as a single unit. In *E. coli*, each series of temperate viruses in the chromosomal phase occupies a specific position. However, they are not incorporated into the bacterial chromosome in the sense that one allele is substituted for another at a chromosomal locus. They are rather supernumerary additions to the chromosomal genetic material. In the extrachromosomal phase, the virus genetic material has two functions, its own replication and the production of nongenetic protein material that is part of the mature virus. In the chromosomal phase, the latter function is not exercised. In fact, in this phase the virus confers immunity on the host because it suppresses the production of protein material by any homologous virus that enters the cell.

A changeover can occur between the chromosomal and the extrachromosomal phases. This requires a breakdown of the immunity reaction, so that the protein material of the mature, infectious virus can be synthesized and, of course, a rupture of the virus-chromosome association effected. This is a rare event, but wholesale conversion of a population of cells containing the virus in the chromosomal phase can be brought about by exposure of the cells to ultraviolet light, X

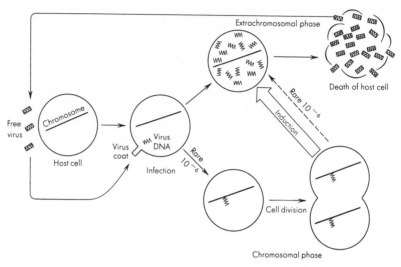

Fig. 9.2. Typical life cycle of a temperate virus of *Escherichia coli*, showing the *relationships* between the free virus in the chromosomal and the extrachromosomal phases. Based on François Jacob and E. L. Wollman, "Genetic Aspects of Lysogeny," in *The Chemical Basis of Heredity* (Johns Hopkins Press, 1957).

rays, and various chemicals. Thus the induction of the extrachromosomal phase has much in common with the induction of phenocopies, dauermodifications, and some extrachromosomal mutants.

Sex factor

The evidence for nonviral episomes is more conjectural, but it is of more direct importance to our study of the extrachromosomal system. Two examples have been described, the "sex factor" and the "colicinogenic factors," both of which have been most fully investigated in strains of *Escherichia coli*.

Conjugation in *E. coli* is between two sexually differentiated cells, in that the "male" donates genetic material to the "female" recipient. This difference has been ascribed to a sex factor, F, which is present in males (F^+) but not in females (F^-).

In a population of males rare females arise, but in a population of females, males do not occur. The transition from male to female has been considered to result from the irreversible loss of the sex factor.

Many types of male are known, the two most important being the normal F^+ and the variant Hfr. F^+ males convert F^- females with a high efficiency into males of the same type, presumably by transferring the sex factor during cell conjugation. In these males, the sex factor appears to exist in an autonomous, extrachromosomal state, behaving as though it were not attached to the chromosome of the male cell, and the speed with which it spreads throughout an F^- female population suggests that the donor cells possess many copies of the sex factor. The sex factor can be eliminated in F^+ males by growing them in the presence of acridine dyes. (See Chapters 6 and 7.)

Hfr males do not convert F^- females into males. It is suggested, therefore, that their sex factor is integrated into the chromosome. This is supported by the segregation of *Hfr* as though it were a chromosomal locus in *Hfr-F^-* crosses. The fact that *Hfr* males do not carry the sex factor in its extrachromosomal state suggests that the two alternative states, as in the case of the temperate viruses, are mutually exclusive.

Each state may spontaneously give rise to the other. F^+ variants occur with varying frequencies in different *Hfr* strains, while *Hfr* variants occur in F^+ strains at the rate of 10^{-4} per cell, per division.

If we accept this explanation of the relationship between F^-, F^+, and *Hfr* strains, then it follows that sexual differentiation in *E. coli* is controlled not by the chromosomal or extrachromosomal cell complement but by an episomic factor. The point of attachment of the sex factor, as shown by its segregation relative to other chromosomal markers, appears to vary in independently isolated *Hfr* strains. Apart from this variation, there is a close parallel between the behavior of the sex factor and the temperate viruses.

Colicinogenic factors

Colicinogenic factors control the production of colicins, which are proteinaceous substances produced by some *Escherichia* strains and able to kill other related strains. In *E. coli*, strain K.30, the inheritance of this property has been worked out largely by P. Frédéricq.

The evidence for the existence of an autonomous extrachromosomal state exactly parallels the evidence obtained for the sex factor. The evidence for the existence of an integrated chromosomal state, however, is more tenuous, since it depends on peculiar properties of sexual recombination in *E. coli*. Thus the frequency, speed, and order with which different chromosomal loci are transferred from *Hfr* to F^- cells vary from one *Hfr* strain to another. Since the transmission of the ability to produce colicin from an *Hfr* to an F^- strain varies from one *Hfr* strain to another in a similar way, it has been inferred that the colicinogenic factor can occupy a locus on the *Hfr* chromosome.

The addition and exchange of hereditary material

It is too early to judge the probable significance of episomes. At the present time, the best evidence for their existence comes from the studies of *E. coli*, where the criteria for separating chromosomal and extrachromosomal phenomena are probably among the least satisfactory to be found. The evidence for nonviral episomes is, therefore, far from compelling. Nevertheless, episomes are conceptually satisfying; they complete the possible relationships between chromosomal gene, extrachromosomal plasmagene, and viral genetic material. Through their intermediary episome, hereditary information from any one of these could be obtained from or transferred to the other two. The temperate virus λ shows us how this could occur.

The wild-type virus can exist in all three states. A mutation in the c region of the virus genome removes the possibility of attachment to give the chromosomal phase. On the other hand, a mutation in the ind region produces an attached chromosomal phase that can no longer be induced to break down by ultraviolet light. Thus from these changes produced by single gene mutations in different regions of the virus genome, we can see how a permanent viral state or a permanent chromosomal attachment could evolve from the initial episomic element.

This latter possibility raises an interesting point. Extrachromosomal heredity is often discounted because, it is claimed, the genetic particles involved were once, or still are, parasites and symbionts of extraneous origin. Clearly, the same argument can be leveled against chromosomal heredity. Viral genetic material can become attached to the chromosome material of bacteria, where it behaves as an integral part of the chromosome complement during cell division. By internal changes in the viral genome, it could become attached permanently. Furthermore, an episomic element can act as a vector for the infective transfer of chromosomal genes from a former host to a new host cell, a phenomenon known as transduction. (See Stahl's *The Mechanics of Inheritance.*)

Hence both foreign bacterial genetic material and viral genetic material may by infection become permanently incorporated into the chromosome of the host. In lower organisms, therefore, the chromosomes are as open to the accretion of new material by infection as is the extrachromosomal complement. If the addition of extraneous hereditary material discredits extrachromosomal heredity, it also discredits chromosomal heredity to a similar extent.

As geneticists, we are ultimately interested in the origin of the hereditary material whose properties we are describing. In this context it matters that infection has played a role. But once the infective material has been incorporated into the permanent hereditary complement of the host, it matters only whether this is transmitted to future generations according to the rules of chromosomal—or to those of extrachromosomal—heredity. Where, however, integration of the viral genetic information is incomplete, and the hereditary material may still revert to its viral form, then its origin is still important to our understanding of its hereditary transmission. Such a situation has been claimed for CO_2 sensitivity in *Drosophila*.

The rho condition, in which flies are resistant to CO_2 but immune to infection, has been likened to the provirus chromosomal phase. The onset of CO_2 sensitivity and the production of infectious particles as the flies age has been likened to its breakdown, giving the virus extrachromosomal phase. This interpretation is strictly by analogy. No integrated phase has been demonstrated, even though the techniques for doing so in *Drosophila* are unrivaled. Nevertheless, it is a satisfactory explanation of the available information—but so, too, is one based on the mutation of a normal extrachromosomal cell component to a suppressive form. It could hardly be otherwise, in view of the many similarities between the properties of episomic viruses and suppressive extrachromosomal mutants. We can, however, be confident of detecting both and often of distinguishing between them by the kinds of criteria currently used in the study of extrachromosomal heredity.

The more important aspect of the episome concept, however, is the possibility that nonviral hereditary material may be exchanged between the chromosomal and extrachromosomal components of the cell. The implication of this is twofold. First, there is the possibility that the same genetic information may be transmitted chromosomally at one time and extrachromosomally at another time; of this possibility we have no evidence among our present-day examples of extrachromosomal heredity. Second, there is the possibility that all the extrachromosomal genetic information originated as episomic elements that have been detached from the chromosomal phase at some stage of evolution. Equally, of course, the chromosomal system could have evolved by the accretion of episomic elements from the extrachromosomal system. There is also another possibility, namely, that episomic elements represent the primitive state from which both the chromosomal and extrachromosomal systems have evolved. By this last interpretation, the present-day examples represent either a continuation of a primitive condition or, alternatively, a return to a primitive condition because of a breakdown in cellular organization. There are other possibilities. It could be, for example, that the random, mutationlike alternation of phase shown by the bacterial episomes has evolved into an orderly alternation that occurs regularly at particular stages or in particular tissues during the development of higher organisms. We do not have confirmation for any of these possibilities, but if episomes have any significance, these are the directions in which it probably lies.

Conclusions

So far three categories of determinants of traits that show extrachromosomal inheritance have been recognized: (1) permanent, extrachromosomal constituents of normal cells that possess genetic continuity; (2) intracellular symbionts and parasites that occupy an extrachromosomal site in the cell; and (3) the extrachromosomal phase of an episome that is extraneous, extrachromosomal, or chromosomal in origin.

The last two categories are known with certainty only in unicellular organisms, where hereditary symbiosis is relatively common. In theory, we can distinguish between the first and last two categories of determinants on a number of criteria. In practice, this distinction is not always easy. It has been suggested that all extrachromosomal determinants belong to the second category or were at least evolved from such a beginning. Although the latter remains a possibility, it must be remembered that intracellular symbionts and parasites appear also to enrich the hereditary material of the chromosomal complement.

The ability of the breeding tests for extrachromosomal heredity to locate correctly the extrachromosomal site of the symbionts and parasites greatly strengthens our confidence in their ability to detect extrachromosomal determinants.

References

Darlington, Cyril D., "Heredity, Development, and Infection," *Nature, 154* (1944), 164.

Jacob, François, P. Schaeffer, and E. L. Wollman, "Episomic Elements in Bacteria," in *Microbial Genetics*, William Hayes and R. C. Clowes, eds. (New York: Cambridge University Press, 1960), p. 67.

Seecof, R. L., "CO_2 Sensitivity in *Drosophila* as a Latent Virus Infection," *Cold Spring Harbor Symp. Quant. Biol., 27* (1962), 501.

Sonneborn, Tracy M., "Gene and Cytoplasm, I and II," *Proc. Nat. Acad. Sci. U.S., 29* (1943), 329.

Questions

9.1. In crosses between killer and sensitive strains of *Paramecium aurelia*, the inheritance of the killer trait satisfies all the criteria of extrachromosomal heredity. Why, therefore, is it claimed that its extrachromosomal determinant, kappa, is a viruslike parasite?

9.2. What properties of unicellular organisms make them particularly susceptible to the initiation and perpetuation of intracellular symbiotic associations that show hereditary transmission?

9.3. What is the basis for the claim that episomes bridge the gap between the extrachromosomal and chromosomal systems?

Gene Dependence of the
Extrachromosomal System

Although the emphasis so far has been on the role of
extrachromosomal determinants in heredity, there has
been occasion to note their apparent dependence on chromosomal genes in their variation, action, and reproduction. The details of the relationship between chromosomal
and extrachromosomal determinants have been worked
out in only a few instances. However, these cases are
sufficient to show a complex interdependence between the
two systems.

Chromosomal–extrachromosomal mimics

Gene and plasmagene mutations often lead to
similar phenotypic changes. Chapters 3 and 4 show, for
example, that variants of green plants that have morphologically and functionally abnormal plastids or that
are male-sterile may result either from extrachromosomally or from chromosomally inherited mutations.

In yeast, petite phenotypes result either from gene
mutations or from plasmagene mutations. The former are
usually known as segregational petites. In *Neurospora*,
gene mutations C115 and C117 result in respiratory upsets similar to those produced by extrachromosomally inherited *mi* mutants. In both yeast and *Neurospora*, the
similarity between the phenotypic effects of these gene
and plasmagene mutations extends to the level of the
enzyme systems associated with the mitochondria. This

is shown most strikingly by spectroscopic analyses of the components of the cytochrome system (see Fig. 3.4). In yeast, gene and plasmagene mutations have very similar effects on the cytochrome system. In *Neurospora*, there are differences in detail, but these are no greater than the differences between the gene mutations C115 and C117, or between the plasmagene mutations, poky and *mi*-3. Thus in yeast and *Neurospora*, the cooperation of both chromosomal and extrachromosomal components is required for the production of a respiratory enzyme system that is functionally normal.

In *Neurospora*, strains carrying both a *mi* mutant and one of the gene mutations, C115 or C117, have been obtained by appropriate crosses (see Fig. 4.3). Spectroscopic analyses of the double mutants (see Fig. 3.4) show that the damage to the cytochrome system is approximately equal to the damage caused by the two-component, single mutations. That is, the effects of the gene and plasmagene mutations are additive.

In *Chlamydomonas reinhardi*, resistance to streptomycin may result either from a single gene or from a plasmagene mutation (see Fig. 4.4). The former, however, confers resistance to only a relatively low concentration of the antibiotic. Jointly, these examples show that both chromosomal and extrachromosomal determinants collaborate to produce many of the phenotypic traits of a normal individual.

Gene-dependent plasmagene action and reproduction

Gene mutations are known that suppress the phenotypic effect of extrachromosomally inherited male sterility in flowering plants, poky mutants of *Neurospora*, and mycelial variants of *Aspergillus nidulans*. In each case, a single chromosomal gene mutation restores the variant phenotype to wild type. These suppressors modify the action of the mutant plasmagenes, but they do not affect their replication or their stability. Hence if, by appropriate breeding procedures, the mutant plasmagene is reassociated with a wild-type chromosomal complement, its effect on the phenotype is restored immediately. A mutant plasmagene, therefore, survives an association with a suppressor gene without being altered, even though its characteristic effect on the phenotype is eliminated throughout the period of association.

Spectroscopic analyses of suppressed poky strains of *Neurospora* show a partial expression of all the characteristic cytochrome abnormalities of the original poky mutant, although, of course, the gross phenotype is wild type. Here we have a direct demonstration that the mutant plasmagene is unaltered in the suppressed state. Since the suppressor is obviously not blocking the action of the mutant plasmagene nor restoring it to that of its wild-type homologue, it must be compensating for the action of the mutant plasmagene.

A different mechanism of suppression is suggested by the chromatographic analyses of male-fertile and male-sterile lines of maize, carried out by Donald F. Jones, H. T. Stinson, and Uheng Khoo. The mature anthers of plants that have an extrachromosomally inherited male sterility lack proline and accumulate asparagine. The mature anthers of male-fertile plants, whether from wild-type or suppressed male-sterile lines, however, contain proline but less asparagine. Thus in this instance, the suppressor genes remove or block the effects of the mutant plasmagenes and allow normal development.

Suppressors vary in their specificities. The suppressor of poky, *f*, is highly specific. It has no effect on any other known mutant, chromosomal or extrachromosomal, that affects the respiratory system of *N. crassa*. The suppressor, therefore, distinguishes between the functional upset produced by poky and that produced by the other respiratory mutations. Suppressors of male sterility in maize are also highly specific. No one suppressor will restore all of the large number of male-sterile strains to fertility. Thus the independent plasmagene mutations have sufficient functional differences to have different spectra of gene suppressors.

Not all gene modifiers of the action of plasmagenes are suppressors. In *Chlamydomonas reinhardi*, Ruth Sager has obtained a gene mutation known as "augmenter," which enhances the dose of streptomycin that all known streptomycin-resistant strains can tolerate. The augmenter has no effect alone, that is, it confers no resistance on the wild-type, streptomycin-sensitive strains. But it is not specific. All resistant mutants, whether chromosomal or extrachromosomal, have a higher tolerance in combination with the augmenter than they have in combination with its wild-type allele.

Stability

In some instances, the chromosomal genes exert their influence on the extrachromosomal system by altering the reproduction and stability of its components. The foremost example of the latter is provided by the iojap gene in maize. Iojap is a recessive gene that gives rise to white, striped plants when homozygous. The inheritance of this striping, which has been extensively studied by Marcus M. Rhoades, is illustrated in Fig. 10.1. When he crossed a striped plant with pollen from a noniojap green plant, either the offspring were all green or they included green, white, and striped plants in widely differing proportions. Occasionally, all the progeny were white, but this was rare. The plants from a reciprocal cross using pollen from the striped plant were always green. The white plants were lethal and could not be tested further, but the striped progeny were viable. If these plants were once more crossed by pollen from a noniojap green plant, the progeny again were all green, all white, or a mixture of green, white, and striped. In all these progeny, half the plants were homozygous for the noniojap gene. Even in the all-white progeny, half the plants that possessed only abnormal white plastids did not have the iojap gene. After repeated backcrossing of the striped plants to pollen from noniojap green plants, progeny containing only white or white, striped, and green plants were still produced, even though by this time very few of the plants contained the iojap gene. A further observation made by Rhoades was that all-white progeny arise when a pollinated flower is situated on a white sector of a striped plant and all-green progeny arise from flowers on green sectors of the same plant.

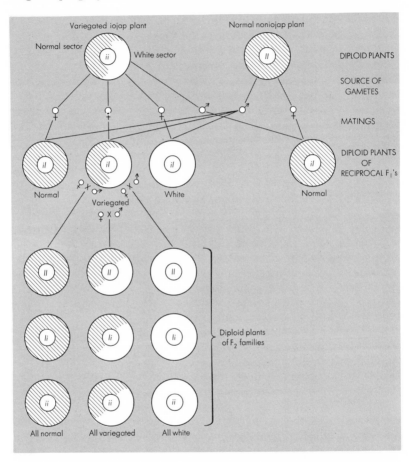

Fig. 10.1. Maize plants that are homozygous for the recessive iojap allele (*ii*) show plastid variegation. When crossed to the normal plants (*II*), however, the variegation shows strict maternal inheritance. The variegation is induced by the homozygous iojap condition, but its subsequent inheritance is strictly extrachromosomal, and it persists in the absence of the iojap allele. Based on Marcus M. Rhoades, "Plastid Mutations," *Cold Spring Harbor Symp. Quant. Biol.,* 11 (1946).

The iojap allele clearly induces irreversible changes in the plastids, and these retain their changed characteristics even when the inducing gene has been wholly replaced by the noniojap allele. The determinants of the altered plastid phenotype show maternal inheritance, hence a genically induced, extrachromosomally inherited change has occurred. Whether these determinants are borne on the plastids or elsewhere in the extrachromosomal complement has not been settled. Mixed cells containing both normal and abnormal plastids have not been demonstrated, but the minute size of abnormal plastids makes it difficult to rule out their presence in cells that apparently contain only normal plastids.

The iojap gene is not unique. Genes that induce similar abnormal plastid phenotypes are known in *Nepeta,* barley, and rice, and in some of these mixed cells have been observed. Hence it has been claimed that the induced changes involve plastogenes. Whether or not this is so, there can be no doubt that certain plasmagenes are unstable, or highly mutable, in association with particular chromosomal genes. Furthermore, these genes show some measure of specificity. The iojap allele, for example, has no effect in the extrachromosomal complement of teosinte maize. On the other hand, this allele is nonspecific in that it also leads to a high frequency of extrachromosomally inherited male-sterility.

Replication

The most fully investigated example of chromosomal gene control of the reproduction of plasmagenes is provided by recent studies on the effect of various mutant genes on the stability of the red variant of *Aspergillus nidulans,* carried out by Morris Grindle, C. F. Arlett, and myself. Mutant genes were associated with the red variant in two ways, but with similar consequences. Some were induced by irradiating the red variant; others were introduced by reassorting the extrachromosomal complement of the red variant with the genome of a strain that carried known gene mutations via the intermediary of heterokaryosis. The majority of the mutant genes led to alterations in the characteristics of the red variant.

The mutant genes could be classified into two groups (Fig. 10.2). The first group, which includes many morphological mutants, such as diffuse and compact, led to a loss of the ability of the red variant to show persistent segregation. Following their introduction, the asexual progeny of the red variant no longer segregated into normal and red phenotypes (see Fig. 5.3). Instead, it gave exclusively colonies with red phenotypes that bred true. Immediately after the introduction of the mutant genes in this group, however, there was an intermediate state, of variable duration, during which the asexual progeny still segregated into normal and red phenotypes. But their breeding behavior was not like that of the same segregants from the original red variant. The normal segregants were slow-growing, and all gave faster-growing red sectors, which soon took over the whole growing front of the colonies. Similarly, the composition of successive samples of the asexual progeny produced by these normal segregants changed from a mixture of normal and red colonies to exclusively red colonies. The red segregants, on the other hand, were completely stable and at all times gave only red colonies in their asexual progeny.

The second group includes spore color mutants, biochemical mutants, and some morphological mutants. These also lead to a loss of the ability of the red variant to show persistent segregation, but they do so in a way opposite to that of the first group. Thus sooner or later after the introduction of the mutant into the red variant, it became

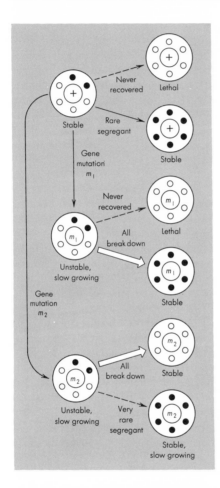

Fig. 10.2. The properties of the red variant of *Aspergillus nidulans,* and their modification by chromosomal gene mutations (m_1 and m_2). The persistent heteroplasmic state of the original red variant is represented as a mixture of two wild-type and four mutant homologues of the determinant. The only stable state, apart from the heteroplasmon itself, is the rarely formed, homoplasmic wild-type segregant. Following the introduction of m_1 or m_2, the heteroplasmon is unstable. It breaks down immediately to give the homoplasmic wild-type or mutant condition, respectively. Based on C. F. Arlett, Morris Grindle, and John L. Jinks, "The Red Cytoplasmic Variant of *Aspergillus nidulans,*" *Heredity, 17* (1962), and Morris Grindle, "Nucleo-cytoplasmic Interactions in the Red Cytoplasmic Variant of *Aspergillus nidulans,*" *Heredity, 19* (1964).

pure-breeding normal. Before this happened, however, it was often possible to obtain a segregation in the asexual progeny into normal and red phenotypes. But these were not typical. The normal segregants were stable and pure-breeding. The red segregants, on the other hand, were slow-growing, unstable colonies; they invariably produced faster-growing normal sectors, which outgrew them. At the same time, the asexual progeny of these red segregants, which initially segregated again, gradually became exclusively normal in phenotype and in breeding behavior.

Chapter 8 shows that the original red variant behaves like a stable heteroplasmon between a lethal suppressive mutant and its normal homologue. The stability results from the conflicting pressures of the suppressive action of the mutant determinant increasing its concentration, on the one hand, and its ultimate dependence on the presence of its normal homologue for survival, on the other. The presence of the first group of mutant genes in the genome of the red variant changes it to a pure-breeding strain with a red phenotype. These genes, therefore, must allow the mutant determinant to suppress completely its normal homologue. To achieve this, the gene must overcome the lethality of the mutant determinant, so that the limitation imposed on its suppressive action by its dependence on the normal homologue is removed. The presence of the second group of mutant genes in the genome of the red variant, however, produces the more interesting result. They change the stable heteroplasmon into a pure-breeding strain with a normal phenotype. This could only be achieved by reversing the roles of the suppressor and the suppressed, that is, by increasing the rate of replication of the normal determinant relative to that of its mutant homologue. Thus when a mutant of the first group is present in the genome of the red variant, the mutant form of the determinant completely replaces its normal homologue in the heteroplasmon; when a mutant of the second group is present, the normal form of the determinant completely replaces its mutant homologue. It appears, therefore, that the relative rates of replication of the mutant and the normal homologue of the determinant are under genotypic control.

A further point arises from these investigations. The extrachromosomally inherited minute variant was induced in the same strain as the red variant. They both have, therefore, the same genome. But while the red variant is a stable heteroplasmon in association with this genome, the minute variant is unstable. In fact, the minute variant behaves more like the red variant when in association with a mutant gene from group two. On the other hand, the mutant genes that bring about a breakdown in the stability of the red variant have no effect on the stability of the purple variant. There is, therefore, some measure of specificity in this interaction between chromosomal genes and extrachromosomal stability. A gene that increases the rate of replication of the mutant form of one determinant relative to its normal homologue has the reverse effect on a different mutant and its normal homologue, and no effect on another.

Conclusions

The occurrence of identical phenotypic changes as a result of gene and plasmagene mutations suggests that the collaboration between the chromosomal and extrachromosomal systems is an equal partnership. On the other hand, the examples just described show that chromosomal genes may override their extrachromosomal partners, for wherever an adequate investigation has been carried out, it has been found that the action, stability, and reproduction of extrachromosomal determinants are under chromosomal gene control, or require the cooperation of chromosomal genes to carry out their normal functions.

For the majority of examples of extrachromosomal inheritance, however, we have no evidence of gene dependence. But we cannot assume that in these instances the extrachromosomal component is independent of gene control. Indeed, we can never prove the independence of any system. To quote Ephrussi: "The demonstration of the dependence of any cell element on the genes is entirely subject to the accident of discovering a chromosomal constitution which interferes with the normal multiplication or the normal functioning of the element in question. Consequently an apparent autonomy can always be ascribed to the fact that the proper chromosomal constitution has not yet been discovered."

References

Grindle, Morris, "Nucleo-cytoplasmic Interactions in the 'Red' Cytoplasmic Variant of *Aspergillus nidulans*," *Heredity, 19* (1964).

Khoo, Uheng, and H. T. Stinson, "Free Amino Acid Differences Between Cytoplasmic Male Sterile and Normal Fertile Anthers," *Proc. Nat. Acad. Sci. U.S., 43* (1957), 603.

Mitchell, Mary B., and Herschel K. Mitchell, "A Nuclear Gene Suppressor of a Cytoplasmically Inherited Character in *Neurospora crassa*," *J. Gen. Microbiol., 14* (1956), 84.

Questions

10.1. Two almost male-sterile strains, A and B, were reciprocally crossed to a fully male-fertile strain, C, with the following consequences.

A female × C male → fully fertile F_1
C female × A male → fully fertile F_1
B female × C male → male-sterile F_1
C female × B male → fully fertile F_1

Backcrosses of either of the fully fertile F_1's obtained by crossing A × C to strain A gave progeny in which half were fully male-fertile and half almost male-sterile. Repeated backcrossing of the male-sterile F_1 obtained on crossing B female × C male to the male-fertile strain C did not lead to the appearance of fully male-fertile progeny. Suggest genotypes and plasmotypes for strains A, B, and C that are compatible with these results.

Another fully male-fertile strain, D, when crossed reciprocally to strain B gave the following result.

B female × D male → fully fertile F_1
D female × B male → fully fertile F_1

The F_2 raised by selfing the F_1 from B female $\times$ D male gave progeny in which one-quarter of the plants were almost male-sterile. The F_2 raised from the reciprocal cross, however, gave all fully male-fertile progeny. What is the genotype and plasmotype of strain D?

10.2. A spontaneous revertant of an extrachromosomally inherited mutant of *Neurospora crassa* was crossed as perithecial parent to a wild-type strain as conidial parent. Among the eight ascospores in each ascus, four gave wild-type growth and four gave mutant growth. The latter were identical in all respects with the original extrachromosomally inherited mutant. Explain this result. What would you expect if the reciprocal cross were made?

Eleven

Chromosomal–Extrachromosomal Cooperation

The preceding chapter has examined the effects of a mutation in either one or both components of chromosomal–extrachromosomal cooperation. Less specific but equally informative upsets in this cooperation may follow the bringing together of a normal chromosomal complement and a normal extrachromosomal complement from different sources. Extensive surveys of the consequences of bringing together such complements from different varieties, races, and species have been carried out in a number of genera of flowering plants. The following are a few representative examples.

Breakdown of cooperation

Outcrossing

Chapter 3 describes the breakdown in the normal functioning of the plastids of *Oenothera Hookeri* when associated with the hybrid chromosomal complex *Hookeri curvans*, by crossing *O. Hookeri* with pollen from *O. muricata* (see Fig. 3.5). The progeny that possessed this novel combination of plastids and genome died as seedlings. This early finding of O. Renner has recently been extended by W. Stubbe and R. E. Cleland who have, between them, studied almost four thousand combinations of the plastids and genomes of different races of *Oenothera*. On the basis of these studies, five main classes of plastids (I, II, III, IV, and V) and three major chromosome complexes (A, B, and C) have been recognized. Each plastid class has its own distinctive reaction to association with the various combinations of the three complexes. The three classes of plastids are green and functionally normal in association with most of the chromosomal complexes, but certain complexes have an adverse effect when combined with certain classes of plastids. For example, *Hookeri* plastids (Class I) are deleteriously affected whenever a hybrid chromosomal complex is made between a *Hookeri* genome (Complex A) and a *parviflora, argillicola,* or *biennis* chromosomal complex (Complexes B and C). *Strigosa* plastids (Class I) are similarly affected by the same complexes. *Argillicola* plastids (Class V) are more or less functionless when the *argillicola* chromosome complex is combined with those of *Hookeri, strigosa,* or *biennis.* The other classes of plastids (II, III, and IV) are unaffected by most chromosomal complexes, but plastids of Classes II and III find it difficult or impossible to develop chlorophyll in association with chromosomal combinations involving the *biennis* complex.

It is clear from these observations that the plastids and chromosomal complexes of such species of *Oenothera* are mutually adapted for chlorophyll production. In addition, the plastids of one species may function normally with certain chromosomal complexes or combinations of complexes from different species, provided that they belong to particular classes. On the other hand, these same plastids may fail to cooperate with certain chromosomal complexes or combinations of complexes from species belonging to other classes. The phenotypic effect of this failure is the same as that produced by a gene or plasmagene mutation that interferes with normal plastid development. But the abnormal or nonfunctional plastids produced by the breakdown of the cooperation between plastids and genome involve neither chromosomal gene mutations nor extrachromosomal plasmagene mutations. They result solely from changes in the action of unchanged chromosomal and extrachromosomal determinants.

A comprehensive investigation of the effects of bringing together in new combinations the plasmons and genomes of different varieties and species of *Epilobium* has been carried out by Peter Michaelis. To introduce the genome of one species or variety into the plasmon of another, he repeatedly backcrossed the variety or species, which was to contribute the plasmon, as female parent, to pollen from the other, which was to contribute the genome. Thus over a number of backcross generations the genome originally associated with the plasmon is gradually replaced by the foreign genome of the persistent male parent. This substitution, however, is complete only if neither competition nor lethality prevents the approach of the foreign genes to homozygosity. Similarly, the plasmon remains unchanged during the substitution only if the pollen contributes no extrachromosomal determinants to the progeny of the backcrosses. Incomplete substitution of the genome and contamination of the plasmon will lead to the presence of genome and plasmon material in the progeny of the advanced backcross generations that is not foreign to the genome or plasmon. This material, however, will merely minimize the effects of the substitution and thus lead to an underestimate of any failure of the foreign genome to cooperate with the plasmon.

The outcome of substituting a genome of one species of *Epilobium* into the plasmon of another can be illustrated by reference to a cross between *E. hirsutum* and *E. luteum* (Fig. 11.1). To combine a *hirsutum*

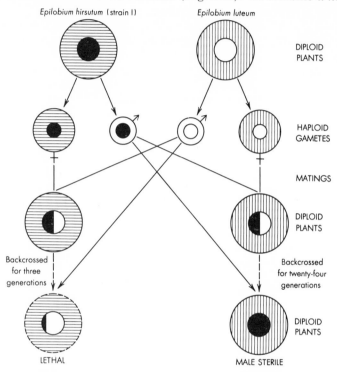

Fig. 11.1. The consequences of complete or partial substitution of the genome of *Epilobium hirsutum* in the plasmon of *E. luteum,* and vice versa. The substitution is achieved by repeated backcrossing into the plasmon of the maternal parent. Based on Peter Michaelis, "Cytoplasmic Inheritance in *Epilobium* and Its Theoretical Significance," *Advan. Genet., 6* (1954).

genome with a *luteum* plasmon, plants of *E. luteum* were used as mothers in crosses to plants of *E. hirsutum* as fathers, and the progeny were repeatedly backcrossed to *E. hirsutum* as fathers. Many independent backcross lines were established, but after the eighth backcross they were all alike, and selection for the next three years could not distinguish between them. Some of these backcross lines were carried on to the fourteenth and others to the twenty-fourth generation of backcrossing. The plants of the advanced backcross generations were similar to the *E. hirsutum* parents, which had supplied most if not all their genome, but they were almost entirely male-sterile. Thus the *hirsutum* genome in a *luteum* plasmon is male-sterile. Male sterility, as we have previously seen in Chapters 4 and 10, can arise as a result of a single gene or plasmagene mutation.

Attempts to introduce a *luteum* genome into the plasmon of two different strains of *E. hirsutum*, strains I and Munich, failed because of the lethality of the third backcross generation with the former strain, and because of the sterility and flower reduction with the latter strain. Thus, they failed because even a partial substitution of a *luteum* genome was sufficient to cause lethal reactions with the *hirsutum* plasmon.

Comparable phenotypic abnormalities occur following the substitution of the genome of one strain of *E. hirsutum* into the plasmon of another. Michaelis has investigated the consequences of substituting the genome of forty different strains of this species into the plasmons of thirty-two different strains. In most cases, the genome was backcrossed into the plasmon for three to eleven generations, but in some cases the backcrossing was continued for as many as twenty-four generations. The phenotypic effects of these substitutions vary. For example, the genome of strain Jena in the plasmon of strain Munich gave normal plants, but the reciprocal combination gave stunted growth. The genome of strain Caen in the plasmon of strain *Insel candidum* gave male-sterile plants, and the genome of strain Kew *alb* in a plasmon of strain Vienna produced plants with deformed flowers.

In the combinations found in nature, the genomes and plasmons of *E. hirsutum* are mutually adjusted to produce a normal phenotype. But in some of the novel combinations produced by these substitutions, the genomes and plasmons are unable to cooperate and the result is an abnormal phenotype. These results do not tell us whether the phenotypic abnormalities are due to the suppression of normal gene action by the foreign plasmon or to the suppression of normal plasmagene action by the foreign genome.

Some of the results of the *Epilobium* crosses suggest that the plasmon may be suppressing the normal action of the foreign genes. Thus the phenotypic effects of the substitutions appear to be more characteristic of the plasmon component than they are of the genomes associated with it. For example, foreign genomes in the plasmon of strain Jena generally produce vegetative disturbances, and pollen sterility is only a secondary effect in those combinations where the vegetative disturbances are particularly marked. In contrast, foreign genomes in the plasmons of the two Greek strains, Xanthe and Attica, cause pollen sterility in even the slightest affected cases, and vegetative disturbances are only encountered in those combinations where the pollen sterility is most extreme. The Jena plasmon appears to inhibit preferentially the genes concerned with vegetative development. The Xanthe and Attica plasmons, on the other hand, seem to inhibit preferentially those responsible for male fertility. Hence a specific plasmon is apparently modifying the action of specific genes.

Evidence for the existence of genes whose action is dependent on the plasmon has been obtained in a number of species. The clearest examples, of course, are those in which a single gene is involved. A typical instance is the recessive *deformatum* gene of strain Kew *alb.* This gene has no known action in its own plasmon, but in the homozygous condition in a Vienna or Giessen plasmon it produces deformed flowers. A further instance is a single recessive gene of tall flax, which produces male sterility in the plasmon of procumbent flax. Similar cases of male sterility in *Nicotiana, Dactylis,* and sugar beet have also been traced to single genes whose action is modified by a foreign plasmon. Of sixty-seven induced gene mutations in *Epilobium parviflorum,* three were sensitive to the plasmon of *E. hirsutum.* The hybrids with the *parviflorum* plasmon attained the normal height of 50 cm., while the reciprocal hybrids with the *hirsutum* plasmon were dwarfs, a few centimeters in height.

The more complex differences between reciprocal crosses of *Epilobium* species, or between strains of *E. hirsutum,* can also be explained in terms of plasmon-sensitive genes. In these cases, however, the action of many genes contributed by the paternal parent are presumably modified by the maternal plasmon. Support for this interpretation is provided by an investigation of the cross between the Jena and Parys strains of *E. hirsutum.*

The hybrid genome in the Parys plasmon is normal; the reciprocal in the Jena plasmon dies as an embryo. By repeatedly selfing and backcrossing the normal hybrid, segregants were obtained that differed in height, growth form, leaf shape, hairiness, flower size, and color. After four generations, a large sample of these segregants was crossed into a Jena plasmon. Almost all produced abnormal progeny; in fact, only a few segregants, which were identical in phenotype with the Jena strain, gave completely normal progeny in the Jena plasmon. Thus the majority of the segregants must have contained at least one gene from the Parys strain that reacted unfavorably with the Jena plasmon.

Since the genomes of these segregants produced widely different phenotypic upsets when crossed into a Jena plasmon, it follows that the Parys strain must contain many genes that react unfavorably to a Jena plasmon. Hence the lethality of the hybrid genome in the Jena plasmon is not due to the reaction of a single gene of the Parys strain to the foreign plasmon, but to the cumulative reaction of many genes, each having a relatively small effect.

Further evidence of the inactivation of genes in a foreign plasmon has been obtained by Fritz von Wettstein and his colleagues in the mosses *Funaria* and *Physcomitrium.* In the offspring of the reciprocal crosses between *F. hygrometrica* and *F. meriterranea,* the alleles contributed by the paternal parent have little or no effect in the plasmon of the maternal species. Similarly, the characteristic effect of genes of *F. hygrometrica* on cell size and the osmotic value of the cells is suppressed in the plasmon of *P. piriforme.*

Only two clear examples of plasmon-sensitive genes are known in the fungi. Both were recently described by Adrian M. Srb, and they involve single gene mutants of *Neurospora*. The first of these is a mutant of *N. sitophila* known as aconidial. In the plasmon of this species the colonies produce no conidia. If, by repeated backcrossing, this mutant gene is placed in the plasmon of *N. crassa*, it has no effect on conidial production. Similarly, a gene, *S*, produces small colonies in the plasmon of the Philippine strain of *N. crassa*. It has no effect, however, in the plasmon of the common laboratory strain of this species. Thus the action of aconidial and *S* is completely inhibited in the foreign plasmon.

Nuclear exchange

In animals, the nature of the interactions between genome and plasmon have been investigated by nuclear transplantations, that is, by the mechanical exchange of nuclei from different uninucleate cells. The favorite cells for such studies are those of the uninucleate amoebae and the eggs of amphibians. When nuclei are exchanged between amoebae belonging to the same clone (homotransfers), the normal activity of the animals is immediately resumed, and they are indistinguishable from unoperated members of the same clone in their subsequent behavior. Clearly, the technique itself has no temporary or permanent effect on the cell phenotype. When, however, the exchange is between animals from different clones (heterotransfers), only a small proportion are able to grow and divide and very few survive to produce a new clone.

I. J. Lorch and J. F. Danielli have studied the short- and long-term results of exchanging the nuclei of two species of *Amoeba*, namely, *A. discoides and A. proteus*. The diameters of nuclei are on averages 38 μ for *A. discoides* and 45 μ for *A. proteus*. Following nuclear exchange between these two species the average nuclear diameter is typical of the species from which the cytoplasm was derived. Thus, immediately after transfer the nuclear diameter is under extranuclear control. *A. proteus* is typically unserrated with few pseudopodia, while *A. discoides* is serrated and has several pseudopodia. A few days after the transplantation of *discoides* nuclei into *proteus* cytoplasms, the animals take on a shape that is wholly typical of *A. proteus*.

The complete extranuclear determination of nuclear size and animal shape is a relatively short-term effect, and the majority of animals on which it has been observed do not survive for any longer-term effects to be investigated. Occasionally, however, an animal survives and produces a clone by binary fission. One such clone, resulting from the transfer of a *proteus* nucleus into a *discoides* cytoplasm, has been studied for many years by Danielli and his colleagues. For nuclear size, the complete extranuclear control persists indefinitely. For animal shape, however, there is a gradual shift toward a shape intermediate between that of the two species, although there is a slight but persistent tendency for it to be more like the species that provided the cytoplasm.

During the period of observation, the original heterotransfer had undergone at least 600 divisions by binary fission, with a consequent dilution of the substance of the original amoeba by a factor of 2^{600}. Clearly, the persistence of characteristics of the species that supplied the cytoplasm must be attributed to extranuclear determinants. The intermediate characteristics must likewise be attributed to a mutual modification of the action of nuclear and extranuclear determinants while in this novel association.

The technique for interchanging the nuclei of amphibian eggs was developed by Robert W. Briggs and T. J. King to investigate the interaction of nuclear and extranuclear material during development. And, as shown in Chapter 12 (see also Clement Markert's *Developmental Genetics*, in this series), it is in this field that the technique has scored its major successes. It has, however, also been used by Briggs and King and others to investigate the effects of transferring the nucleus of one species into the cytoplasm of another.

The egg of one species or subspecies is enucleated, and the nucleus of a different subspecies, species, or genus is introduced by fertilizing the egg with a sperm from the appropriate source or by injecting a nucleus from an egg or an embryo. In some instances, for example, in the transplantation of nuclei between two subspecies of *Xenopus laevis,* the embryos develop normally and the adults have the characteristics of the subspecies that supplied the nucleus. In general, however, while the early stages of the development of the heterotransfers are normal, sooner or later development ceases. This cessation may occur as early as cleavage if the sources of nucleus and cytoplasm are distantly related, or as late as the blastula or gastrula stages of development if they are more closely related. J. A. Moore has produced evidence that the nuclei of embryos that fail are profoundly altered by their replication in the foreign cytoplasm. Thus nuclei of *Rana pipiens* in the enucleated eggs of *R. sylvaticum* produce an embryo whose development fails at the end of the blastula stage. When the nuclei of these embryos were returned to enucleated eggs of their own species, most failed to develop beyond the gastrula stage. A similar sequence of nuclear transfers of *pipiens* nuclei in *pipiens* enucleated eggs always gave normal development. Moore concluded, therefore, that the *pipiens* nucleus had been permanently changed by the *sylvaticum* cytoplasm. The nature of this change has been shown by the cytological investigations of Sally Hennen. She found that the *pipiens* nuclei, which failed to produce normal development in a *pipiens* cytoplasm after replicating in a *sylvatica* cytoplasm, had abnormal chromosomal complements. They showed varying degrees of aneuploidy and contained morphologically abnormal chromosomes, such as rings and minutes. The occasional *pipiens* nucleus, which could still produce normal development after this treatment, however, had a normal chromosome complement. It appears, therefore, that the stability of the chromosome complement, and hence of the genome, is adversely affected by the foreign extranuclear material.

As shown in Chapter 10, the action, stability, and reproduction of plasmagenes is ultimately under the control of chromosomal genes. Investigations of the effects of associating foreign genomes and plasmons in unusual combinations show further the extent of the interdependence of the two components of the cell. But more important, they show that the action and stability of the genome is subject to the control of the plasmon.

Mechanics of cooperation

From an examination of the relationship between genome and plasmon in a variety of situations, it is clear that they are partners in the determination of the phenotype. Neither partner is dominant, for neither invariably determines the action of the other; rather, they are complementary. Formally, at its simplest, this means that a gene or a number of genes produce a product, A, that in combination with product B, produced by one or many plasmagenes, gives rise to product C. The latter may be the end product of a particular synthetic sequence, or merely the beginning of a further stage in the action and interaction of genes and plasmagenes. If, as a result of gene mutation or the substitution of a different genome, product A either is not produced or is produced in a modified form, then the production of C will be affected. Similarly, a plasmagene mutation or a plasmon substitution that affects the production of B will also interfere with the production of C. This simple model portrays the salient features of the known interactions between genome and plasmon. But what, in fact, are the respective contributions of genes and plasmagenes to their joint action? What is the nature of A and B?

One view is that the genes are responsible for all syntheses, that they supply the building blocks that the plasmagenes assemble. This is the view favored by J. F. Danielli to explain the apparent roles of genome and plasmon in *Amoeba*. Tracy M. Sonneborn also interprets the roles of cortical determinants and genes in the production of the cortex of *Paramecium* along similar lines. According to this view, the plasmagenes are little more than sites or templates for the assembly of gene products. The necessity of having at least one plastid or protoplastid, centriole, and kinetosome present before others can be produced would be similarly explained. That these structures are the sites at which further similar structures are generated or assembled is amply supported by cytological evidence. That the materials necessary for this process are supplied solely by the genes, however, is only speculation.

If, as has been suggested, the hereditary material of plasmagenes is DNA (see Chapter 7), then it would seem reasonable to assume that activities of plasmagenes and chromosomal genes are similar. In this case, if genes synthesize building blocks, presumably plasmagenes can synthesize them also. In some species, the completion of plastid development depends on the photochemical activity of the plastid itself; a light stimulation is necessary for the lamellar discs to take on a parallel arrangement and to multiply. In these species, the immature plastid produces some of the synthetic products required to complete its own structure. A similar conclusion, with respect to the materials required for centriole construction, is suggested by observations on the behavior of centrioles in the enucleated eggs of amphibians. In the absence of the nucleus, the egg is often cleaved in the normal way; the centrioles multiply before each cell division and carry out their usual functions. The whole of the cleavage stage, consisting of many cell divisions, may be completed in this way. It seems unlikely, although, of course, not impossible, that the centrioles could continue their normal replication in these circumstances if they were totally dependent on gene products for their building materials.

Recent work, particularly on bacteria, suggests that there is a special RNA, "messenger RNA," that is synthesized by the genes and released to the microsomes, where it acts as a template for protein synthesis. This RNA appears to turn over very rapidly. It is continually produced and destroyed. It is suggested that another RNA, "transfer RNA," carries the amino acids, the raw materials of protein synthesis, to the microsomes. An RNA fraction with the properties of messenger RNA has now been demonstrated in bacteria, yeasts, and mammalian cells. Furthermore, limited protein synthesis has been achieved in vitro by adding transfer RNA and amino acids to microsomes from these different kinds of cell in the presence of energy sources, such as ATP and GTP. Here, therefore, we have a direct example of an extrachromosomal entity providing the site, and the genes the information, for the assembly of amino acids into proteins. The proteins, in turn, may be used either as building blocks or as mediators of further syntheses. The extrachromosomal entity involved is not one for which there is evidence of genetic continuity, although its origin, as well as its seat of action, is probably extrachromosomal (see Chapter 2).

Not all the extrachromosomal RNA is necessarily genic in origin, and not all protein synthesis that occurs outside the nuclear membrane is necessarily dependent on a labile messenger RNA. On the first point, H. Harris and his collaborators have shown that the extranuclear RNA of rapidly growing mammalian cells in tissue culture may be synthesized from precursors by pathways that do not implicate nuclear RNA. Indeed, nuclear RNA does not appear to be transferred to the cytoplasm in a stable form. On the second point, J. Hammerling showed many years ago that nonnucleated fragments of the alga *Acetabularia* could grow and their chloroplasts increase in number, and biochemical studies have shown that the extranuclear system is capable of independent RNA and protein synthesis. Two weeks after enucleation these synthetic activities come to a standstill, although the fragments may survive for some time afterward. During the first two weeks, however, the protein synthesis, which presumably is mediated by the simultaneously synthesized RNA, can hardly be dependent on a labile messenger RNA produced by the genes. These results must imply a synthetic role for the extrachromosomal system.

References

Briggs, Robert W., and T. J. King, "Changes in the Nuclei of Differentiating Endoderm Cells as Revealed by Nuclear Transplantation," *J. Morphol., 100* (1957), 269.

Danielli, J. F., "Studies of Inheritance in *Amoeba* by the Technique of Nuclear Transfer," *Proc. Roy. Soc. (London), Ser. B, 148* (1958), 321.

Hammerling, J., "Nucleo-cytoplasmic Relationships in the Development of *Acetabularia*," *Intern. Rev. Cytol., 2* (1953), 475.

Michaelis, Peter, "Cytoplasmic Inheritance in *Epilobium* and Its Theoretical Significance," *Advan. Genet., 6* (1954), 287.

Moore, J. A., "Nuclear Transfer of Embryonic Cells of the Amphibia," in *New Approaches in Cell Biology*, P. M. B. Walker, ed. (New York: Academic Press, Inc., 1960), p. 1.

Sonneborn, Tracy M., "The Gene and Cell Differentiation," *Proc. Nat. Acad. Sci. U.S., 46* (1960), 149.

Questions

11.1. How far can the phenotypic abnormalities that often result from outcrossing geographical races of the same species or different species be understood in terms of plasmon-sensitive genes that are inactivated in a foreign plasmon?

11.2. Compare nuclear transplantation, heterokaryosis, and repeated backcrossing as methods for introducing a genome into a foreign plasmon.

Twelve

Extrachromosomal Differences in
Development

The facts presented in earlier chapters show that phenotypic differences between cell lineages of the same organism and differences between whole organisms can result
from purely extrachromosomal changes. Some of these
changes persist, indeed they are as permanent as the
most stable gene mutation. Others are reversible, or subject to environmental modification to an extent that is
rare among chromosomal genes. Some plasmagene mutations produce phenotypic changes that are equivalent to
major gene mutations. Others produce small continuous
differences in phenotype that, like their chromosomal
counterparts, may be accumulated by selection to give
major phenotypic changes. Whether their effect on the
phenotype is discontinuous or continuous, the plasmagenes react on the action of the genome and in turn they
are reacted upon by the genome. These facts should be
kept in mind as the role of extrachromosomal differences
in development, variation, and evolution is examined in
this and the following chapter.

All organisms, whether they are unicellular or multicellular, undergo a process of orderly change or development during the course of their lives. Embryological
studies have described these orderly changes (see Markert's *Developmental Genetics,* in this series), and ge-
netical studies have attempted to elucidate the mechanism of their inheritance. All the suggested mechanisms
have a role for the extrachromosomal cell constituents;

146

they differ only in the importance of this role. And certainly the somatic flexibility of the extrachromosomal system, its capacity for reversible and stable changes, and its interdependence with the chromosomal system for cell metabolism, is a property prospectively required in organism development. The suitability of the extrachromosomal system for a role in development need not, therefore, be stressed; this is self-evident from the earlier chapters. What is pertinent here is the nature of its contribution to development.

Irrespective of the complexity of the developmental pattern of an organism, at some stage in its life cycle it consists of a single cell, the zygote, that is capable of producing the whole complex pattern itself. In some higher plants and animals, attachment to the mother is essential for early development, but the role of the mother appears to be the passive one of supplying protection and food, a role satisfied in other, usually less efficient, ways in lower organisms. In higher organisms, this early dependence on the mother only rarely leads to a lasting effect on the adult phenotype (see Chapter 4). Hence in general the zygote is in itself totipotent, given a suitable environment. The differentiation that occurs during the development of a multicellular organism may, therefore, be regarded as a gradual restriction in different cell lineages of the totipotentialities originally carried in the zygote.

From numerous observations of the chromosome complements of different cells and tissues of single individuals, and of the consequences of accidental or deliberate changes in the chromosomal complement during development, it must be concluded that the presence of a complete, balanced set of chromosomes is required for normal development. Furthermore, changes in this complement are not a regular cause or consequence of differentiation. Any chromosomal changes during development are, therefore, primarily changes in function. If any segregation of heritable information occurs during development, therefore, it must, in general, be confined to information that is extrachromosomally transmitted.

Thomas H. Morgan was one of the first to suggest an explanation of development based on the segregation of heterogeneous extrachromosomal complements. He postulated that the functions of the equipotent chromosomal complements would be modified in different cell lineages by their different extrachromosomal environments. Kenneth Mather subsequently elaborated this hypothesis and made detailed suggestions concerning the mechanism of the chromosomal–extrachromosomal interaction during differentiation. To demonstrate this postulated role of the extrachromosomal system, we require experimental support for each of the following propositions.

(1) Part, at least, of the totipotency of the zygote resides in the extrachromosomal material.

(2) This material segregates to different cells during cleavage, and cells that receive different extrachromosomal material give rise to different kinds of cell lineages.

(3) Some of the differences between the cell lineages and the tissues that arise from them are extrachromosomal.

The kinds of evidence that support these propositions are briefly indicated in the following pages; more detailed accounts will be found in Markert's *Developmental Genetics*.

Totipotency

For technical reasons, most of the information about development comes from animal species that have particularly large zygotes. Most of the material of such zygotes is provided by the egg. And although the sperm contributes mitochondria, remnants of the endoplasmic reticulum, and a centrosome, the successful development of many eggs without fertilization shows that the sperm's contribution is not indispensable for early development. Nor is all the extrachromosomal material of some large eggs essential for development. The egg of the sea urchin *Arbacia* may be divided into two parts by centrifugation, so that one part is free from large granular inclusions such as mitochondria, yolk, and pigment. After fertilization, the free part still develops into small plutei of a fairly normal shape. Although this treatment reduces the amount of large granules in the free part, it does not, however, remove them all, for mitochondria reappear during development. They come, presumably, from smaller, remaining precursors, or perhaps from the sperm.

Numerous observations show that, in the original egg, visibly recognizable regions contain material essential for the normal development of specific organs. For example, removal of the peripheral cytoplasm of ctenophore eggs results in larvae that fail to develop normal swimming plates. Equally, the removal of the white polar lobe of *Dentalium* eggs leads to the absence of the posttrocal region and of the apical organ in the larva. Fragments of amphibian eggs lacking material from the so-called gray crescent region fail to gastrulate, while similar fragments that contain it can give a complete embryo. Since none of these treatments is likely to alter the chromosomal complement (which we know is essential for normal development), we must conclude that the totipotency of the zygote resides partly in the extrachromosomal material.

Many attempts have been made to correlate the distribution of the visible endoplasmic structures of the zygote with the subsequent fate of different parts of the zygote during development. The experiments have used centrifugation and chemical treatments to change the normal distribution of these structures in the zygote. The aim was to see whether this displacement affects development. The results are inconsistent. In some experiments with sea urchin eggs, centrifugation has led to a complete failure of organized differentiation, although there is no obvious relationship between the type of failure and the disturbed distribution of visible extrachromosomal structures. In other experiments, centrifugation has had no effect on development. The latter, however, can be interpreted as evidence that the extrachromosomal information is situated largely in the more rigid ectoplasm.

Gradients of endoplasmic extrachromosomal material are present in most eggs. They may be RNA gradients, as in amphibian eggs, mitochondrial gradients, as in *Arbacia* eggs, or respiratory gradients, probably resulting from an underlying mitochondrial gradient, as in *Mytilus* eggs. As differentiation proceeds, these gradients persist, steepen, or become more complex.

Since opposite poles of the egg have different fates during development, it seems likely that these gradients are intimately concerned with differentiation, either as cause or effect. Chemical treatments of eggs, particularly with lithium salts, disturb these gradients and simultaneously produce abnormal development. For example, if *Arbacia* eggs are treated with lithium salts, the mitochondrial frequency is reduced, while the embryo shows hyperdevelopment of the endoderm at the expense of the ectoderm. From a survey of the manifold and varying effects of lithium on the differentiation of a wide range of invertebrate and vertebrate embryos, T. Gustafson has concluded that it probably always operates by modifying the mitochondrial gradients. In amphibian eggs the RNA gradient, which decreases from the animal to the vegetal pole, is present in unfertilized, fertilized, and cleaving eggs. Female sex hormones alter the RNA gradient during cleavage and, as a consequence, development becomes highly abnormal. Similarly, centrifugation of newly fertilized eggs also modifies the RNA gradient, and this leads to a more or less complete failure of head development. It appears, therefore, that both ectoplasmic and endoplasmic materials contribute to the totipotency of the zygote. Furthermore, at least part of the totipotency is provided by structures such as mitochondria, which either possess genetic continuity or are partially under the control of plasmagenes.

Among the unicellular and some clonal plants and animals, soma, gamete, and zygote are often stages in the development or maturation of one and the same cell. And as the distinction between somatic and germ cells disappears, the contrast between heredity and development breaks down. Thus the demonstration in breeding experiments (see Chapter 3) that the cortical regions of ciliates show genetic continuity is equivalent to showing that the totipotency of the zygote in this group rests partly in the cortical ectoplasm. The same argument, of course, applies equally to the elaborate plastid structures found in unicellular and colonial algae.

In the fungi, there are a number of demonstrations that normal development requires a balanced extrachromosomal as well as a balanced chromosomal complement. Many extrachromosomal variants of fungi are characterized by the failure of particular stages in development. In the more extreme cases, only undifferentiated vegetative hyphae are produced. In the less extreme cases, development is apparently normal, but the final product of the sexual differentiation pattern, the ascospores, are inviable. The same range of developmental upsets also occurs following chromosomal gene mutations. Hence the developmental potential of any inoculum or zygote that can initiate a fungal colony depends on both its chromosomal and extrachromosomal content.

Segregation

At least part of the developmental potential may be stored in the gradients of endoplasmic material and in the patterned ectoplasm of a zygote. But this by itself is not enough. If endoplasmic or ectoplasmic material is to play a role in the complex processes of development, it must segregate or sort out in an orderly manner into different cell lineages of the cleaving zygote (Fig. 12.1). It is, therefore, es-

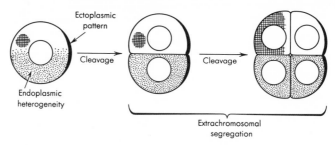

Fig. 12.1. A diagram showing how four different cell lineages could arise during the cleavage of a zygote by the segregation of endoplasmic and ectoplasmic differences.

sential that the planes of cleavage be arranged in predetermined positions relative to the gradients and cortical patterns. Chapter 2 has already shown that in an extrachromosomal body the centriole plays an important role in the control of the position and plane of cleavage.

The relationship between the position of cleavage and the extrachromosomal gradients is important for subsequent development. For example, cleavage in *Mytilus* zygotes is normally unequal. Ultraviolet irradiation and centrifugation will artificially induce equal cleavage of the zygote. As a consequence, each half of the cleaved zygote develops into a complete embryo, producing twins instead of two different cell lineages of a single embryo. Hence, instead of the zygote dividing into two cells with different developmental potentialities, it divides into two equipotent and totipotent halves (Fig. 12.2a).

The plane of cleavage is as important as the position of cleavage relative to the extrachromosomal gradients. For example, in *Ascaris* chromosomal diminution occurs in the cell destined to form the soma, but not in those destined to form the germ cells. In a normal zygote, the first cleavage plane divides it into the so-called animal and vegetal blastomeres. At the beginning of the second division, the chromosome complement of the animal blastomere undergoes diminution, and that of the vegetal blastomeres remains intact. If the uncleaved zygote is centrifuged, it is flattened and the first cleavage occurs at right angles to its normal direction. As a result, the extrachromosomal material that would normally segregate into animal and vegetal halves is divided equally between the two cleavage products. As a consequence, neither chromosomal complement undergoes diminution (Fig. 12.2b).

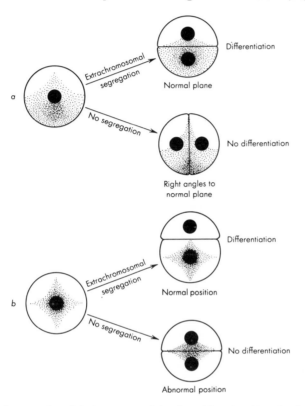

Fig. 2.2. A demonstration of the importance of the plane (a) and position (b) of the cleavage of the zygote, relative to the endoplasmic gradients. An induced change in either may lead to a failure of segregation and hence of differentiation.

The ectoplasmic material also plays a role in determining the position of cleavage. Thus centrifugation of eggs of *Ilyanassa* during the production of the second polar body will shift the spindle from its normal position only if the cortex is somewhat elongated as a result of the treatment. Hence the cortex plays a dominant role in determining the position of cleavage. We may conclude, therefore, that extrachromosomal agents, whether cortical or centriolar, exercise some control over the segregation of extrachromosomal material during cleavage.

There are many observations to show that cells that receive visibly different extrachromosomal complements during cleavage subsequently give rise to different tissues in the embryo. For example, the cell that receives most of the mitochondria during the cleavage of a *Tubifex* zygote gives all the mesoderm of the embryo. Similarly, wherever the oxidative enzymes and, therefore, presumably the mitochondria, accumulate after centrifugation of ascidian zygotes, this is the position where muscle differentiation ultimately occurs. This must mean that a high concentration of oxidative enzymes at the time of cleavage determines the presumptive muscle region. Again, during the cleavage of the zygotes of the ctenophore *Beroë*, there is an unequal partitioning of the mitochondria, which are concentrated very early in the cells that later produce the ciliary plates.

The best example of extrachromosomal determination of subsequent development yet described concerns the differentiation of the germ cells in Cecidomyiidae embryos. By three successive mitotic divisions, the zygotic nucleus gives eight nuclei. These are distributed along the length of the elongated zygote. At one end of the early zygote, a region of the extrachromosomal material is distinguishable by its homogeneity and by the absence of large granules. The nucleus, which happens to lie in this polar region, provides the chromosomal material of the future germ line. The remaining seven nuclei represent the future soma and they, like the somatic nucleus of *Ascaris*, undergo chromosomal diminution to the characteristic complement of somatic cells. Thus a predetermined visible heterogeneity of the extrachromosomal material is apparently responsible for the differentiation of the somatic and germ cell lineages.

It has been proved beyond doubt that there is some substance in the polar region that stops the chromosomal elimination of the future germ line. This substance may be moved by centrifugation, whereupon this property is transferred from the polar region to a new region of the zygote. Hence the substance is functional, even in a presumptive somatic region of the embryo. Although this substance stops chromosome elimination, it does not, however, control the subsequent development of the germ line. This property is retained by the polar region, even after centrifugation. The elimination or nonelimination of the chromosome material plays no immediate role; it is a result, not a cause of differentiation.

These examples are a few of the many that support the idea of a mechanism of differentiation based on the segregation of heterogeneous extrachromosomal material and the modification of the function of equipotent chromosomal complements. Additional support for this mechanism is provided by the examples described in Chapters 10 and 11, which show that the plasmon can modify both gene action and the stability of the chromosomal complement. This mechanism of differentiation does not, of course, require that all the extrachromosomal differences that distinguish the tissues of an adult organism be already present in the zygote, or even in the young embryo. As Kenneth Mather has pointed out, the equipotent chromosomal complements in their different extrachromosomal environments will lead to a further divergence by virtue of their different activities, releasing different products into their environment. And the changed extrachromosomal environment will, in turn, react on the chromosomal activity to modify it further. Chapters 10 and 11 also show that a change in the action of chromosomal genes will modify the action, stability, and replication of extrachromosomal determinants. By these mutual modifications, a small initial difference in the extrachromosomal content of different cell lineages can be successively built up into the larger differences of the adult tissues.

If we accept this explanation, the problem of differentiation, at least in multicellular animals, becomes the problem of the origin of the distribution of extrachromosomal material during the production of the gamete, and more particularly during the production of the egg. There is no direct evidence that extrachromosomal determinants are involved in the extrachromosomal gradients that ultimately depend on quantitative or qualitative differences in RNA and protein, although it is known that active synthesis of both occurs in the cytoplasm during the production of the egg. Since, however, mitochondria and centrioles either possess genetic continuity or their structure and function are partly controlled by plasmagenes, it cannot be doubted that the latter make some contribution to the extrachromosomal heterogeneity upon which differentiation depends. But it is also abundantly clear that chromosomal genes, rather than extrachromosomal plasmagenes, are responsible for the production of much of the extrachromosomal material whose distribution in the egg is the starting point of differentiation.

Tissue differences

There is almost no direct evidence of the nature of the differences between the tissues of higher plants. Most plants can regenerate a completely normal individual from a small fragment, hence it seems unlikely that different organs are differentiated by irreversible changes in either their chromosomal or extrachromosomal complements. There are, however, limitations to this power of regeneration. In some plants —for example, *Gardenia amoena* and Cedar of Lebanon—the growth habit of vegetative propagants varies according to the part of the plant from which the cuttings are made. Obviously, in these two examples persistent changes have accompanied differentiation. The change in phase from a juvenile to a mature growth habit often coincides with an irreversible change. For example, the shoot of the juvenile form of ivy, *Hedera helix,* creeps and roots. The mature flowering shoot loses both capacities, and this loss persists through indefinite periods of propagation by cuttings of the mature form. The change from juvenile to mature is regularly reversed only by sexual reproduction; the seeds from the mature form germinate to give the juvenile form. Artificial treatments will also bring about this reversal; these include shocking with low temperature, X-irradiation, grafting onto a juvenile form, and merely growing the mature form in the same solution as a juvenile form. As Cyril D. Darlington has pointed out, the nature of the artificial treatments that will reverse the change and the spontaneous reversal during sexual reproduction suggests an extrachromosomal basis rather than a chromosomal basis. At the present time, only these indirect suggestions of the basis of differentiation are available in higher plants.

Attempts to propagate from different tissues or from organs of higher animals, if successful, generally produce only cells of the type present in the inoculum. Under suitable conditions, pure cultures (so-called tissue cultures) or different cell types may be obtained and maintained indefinitely. Thus animal tissues, in general, appear to differ irreversibly from one another.

As yet, no method of analyzing the nature of the differences between tissues in culture has been devised. The evidence of its nature is, therefore, necessarily obtained by indirect means. Foremost among these is the transplantation of nuclei from developing embryos into enucleated eggs, as described in Chapter 11. The logic behind this procedure is simple. A nucleus from a developing embryo is substituted for that of an egg. If the latter still develops normally, then it is inferred that the transplanted nucleus cannot have undergone any irreversible change up to the stage in development of the donor embryo at which the transplantation was made. If, on the other hand, the egg does not develop normally, then the transplanted nucleus has presumably changed at some stage in development of the donor embryo prior to the transplantation.

In their first series of experiments with embryos of *Rana pipiens*, T. J. King and Robert W. Briggs transplanted nuclei from fully determined cells of embryos in the late gastrula stage. If these cells were moved intact to a different position, they still developed along their normal pathway. Nevertheless, the nuclei from these cells, when transplanted into enucleated eggs, produced normal larvae in a relatively high percentage of cases. King and Briggs concluded that embryonic cell lineages that were already irreversibly determined contained nuclei that had undergone no irreversible changes.

In a further series of experiments, the fully determined endodermal cells of late gastrulae were used as nuclear donors. Although an improved technique was used and injury during transplantation reduced, fewer of the transplants gave normal larvae. By transplanting nuclei from progressively later embryos, King and Briggs found that, with increasing age, the endodermal nuclei showed progressively less ability to support the normal cleavage of an enucleated zygote. By the time the donor cells reached the tailbud stage, no transplants gave normal larvae. Thus by the end of the gastrula stage some of the nuclei of the endodermal cells had become permanently differentiated because they could no longer support normal differentiation. The observations of King and Briggs leave no doubt that the nucleus ultimately undergoes irreversible changes during the differentiation of *Rana pipiens*. Nor can it be doubted that development up to the gastrula stage in-

volves only extranuclear changes. Even as late as the neurula stage
there is still present a proportion, albeit low, of nuclei that are totipotent. It seems probable, therefore, that some cells in the neurula
that differ only in their extranuclear complement are playing a role in
differentiation.

The recent work of M. Fischberg, T. R. Elsdale, and J. B. Gurdon
suggests that the role of the extranuclear complement may be even
more important in *Xenopus laevis*. Their research technique was somewhat different from Briggs and King's. Briggs and King removed the
nuclear material from the egg into the jelly surrounding it before
introducing the new nucleus, along with its accompanying cytoplasm.
Fischberg and his colleagues did not remove the egg nucleus. They
relied on a number of observations showing that when a nucleus is
injected into a mature egg the resident maternal nucleus does not
contribute to the nuclei of the embryo. In their more recent experiments, the recipient egg was also irradiated for one minute before
introducing the new nucleus. This treatment kills the egg nucleus,
which then degenerates in the egg cytoplasm, but the developmental
potential of the egg following the introduction of another nucleus does
not appear to be impaired. Fischberg had generally less success with
transplants from older embryos than with those from younger embryos. But he did obtain normal larvae from transplants of the mesoderm and endoderm of a neural fold, from the tailbud stage and from
later stages, that showed muscular responses.

The general conclusion is, therefore, that some nuclei are capable
of supporting normal development very shortly before the organ from
which they are obtained becomes functional. This result could be
partly due to a reversal or repair of the lost differentiation potentials
of nuclei from advanced donors by products released by the degenerating egg nucleus; totipotency may have been regained by the transplanted nucleus absorbing from the degenerating egg nucleus certain
substances for which it had become deficient during the course of
differentiation. At the present time, this possibility remains. J. B.
Gurdon, however, has shown that even if the transplanted nucleus
does receive something from the degenerating egg nucleus, the latter
makes no recognizable contribution to the phenotype of the embryo,
larva, or adult that is produced; the latter is always typical of the
strain, variety, or subspecies that donated the nucleus.

The results of nuclear transplantations in *Rana* and *Xenopus* agree
in showing that a certain level of differentiation can occur without
involving any irreversible changes in the nuclear material. The latter
must, therefore, exhibit only reversible changes in function. The stability of the differentiation up to this level, which includes fully
determined, presumptive tissues, can only be the result of extranuclear
differentiation. At a higher level of differentiation, an increasing proportion of nuclei becomes irreversibly changed, but even so, nuclei
taking part in the differentiation may still exhibit only reversible
changes in function. Whether this latter situation extends into fully

functional organs is not clear, and it will remain so until the disparity between the results from *Rana* and *Xenopus* has been explained. Nevertheless, the results from both genera show that a proportion of the nuclei in older embryos undergo irreversible losses in their developmental potentialities. How do these irreversible changes come about?

The irreversible changes in the nuclear material of *Rana* involve no alterations in the chromosome complement. Any explanation must, therefore, depend on irreversible changes in function. If irreversible changes in function are to lead to differentiation, then the genes whose functions are being altered must differ from one presumptive tissue to another. These different responses of the genes must be the result of different stimuli. It is easy to see how the different extrachromosomal material in different cells could provide the necessary stimuli. It is not so easy to see how the stimulus could arise from within the chromosomal complement itself in the first instance, although once the chromosomal complements in different cells had responded differently, this could become the stimulus for further divergence in gene action. Thus the initial irreversible change in gene action is a result, not a cause, of differentiation, which subsequently becomes the cause of further differentiation.

How can a difference between cells that is initially extranuclear in origin subsequently come to depend on a permanent difference in the action of their chromosomal genes? A partial answer is provided by Tracy M. Sonneborn's analysis of mating type in group B animals of *Paramecium aurelia*. Mating type determination in this group is strictly maternal unless there is a considerable exchange of extrachromosomal material between conjugants (see Chapters 4 and 6, and Figs. 3.1 and 6.3). Animals of variety 4 were conjugated, and pairs showing considerable extrachromosomal exchange were selected and exposed to high temperatures long enough to retard the development of the macronuclei but without suppressing them entirely. By this technique Sonneborn was able to obtain, from a given exconjugant, animals with identical micronuclear and extrachromosomal complements but differing in that some had macronuclei derived from the fusion nucleus and some had macronuclei derived from fragments of the old macronucleus. Because of the exchange of extrachromosomal material during conjugation, the former animals were regularly of the mating type of the other parent. But the animals containing a regenerated macronucleus had the same mating type as the parental animal that had supplied the macronucleus fragments. These mating type reactions survived binary fission and autogamy unchanged.

In this experiment and in the experiments described in Chapter 4, Sonneborn demonstrated that a change of mating type at conjugation may be due to the action of foreign extrachromosomal material on a newly developing macronucleus. A mature macronucleus, or a regenerating fragment of a mature macronucleus, however, cannot be modified in this way; its activities are permanently determined by the extrachromosomal complement in which it completed its own early development. Hence in *Paramecium* we find a direct demonstration of the mechanism of differentiation that has been postulated to explain the results of nuclear transplantations in *Rana* and *Xenopus*.

A visual demonstration of the idea that the extrachromosomal complement of different tissue may modify the activity of chromosomal genes in different ways is provided by a series of elegant experiments carried out principally by Wolfgang Beermann and Heinrich Kroeger. Dipteran larvae have salivary glands whose large cells contain enormous chromosomes. These giant chromosomes possess large chromomeres, whose shapes are characteristic of particular sites on the chromosomes. The chromomeres can swell up into so-called balbiani rings or puffs. These puffs are sites of strong RNA and protein synthesis, and their occurrence follows a particular pattern. In a mature larva of a particular species, only certain chromomeres will show puffs, while in young larvae other chromomeres will show puffs. Furthermore, where giant chromosomes have been observed in other tissues besides salivary glands, it is found that the puffs occur at different chromosomal sites in different tissues. Thus the activity of the chromomeres is not only specific with time or age, but also with respect to cell type. It appears, therefore, that particular extrachromosomal complements can call forth the activity of particular chromosomal sites. This conclusion has been confirmed by transferring salivary gland chromosomes to the different extrachromosomal environment of a developing egg. The puffing of certain regions of the chromosomes ceased in this new environment, while other regions were induced to puff. Furthermore, the regions that puffed varied with the developmental stage of the egg that supplied the new extrachromosomal environment. These observations provide the clearest insight yet available into the relationship between extrachromosomal and chromosomal material during development (Fig. 12.3).

Regeneration

Plants do not, in general, replace their damaged or lost parts. Instead, regeneration involves a small part reconstituting the entire organization. Animals, on the other hand, possess varying and often wide powers of replacement or reconstitution of structures from a surviving portion. While we should not push this contrast too far because of the frequent exceptions, especially among lower organisms, it does suggest a basically different pattern of differentiation in animals and plants. But it is more important to the immediate discussion that the regenerative power of animals appears at first sight to rule out any mechanism of differentiation that is irreversible. Is there, in fact, a conflict between the results from nuclear transplantation and regeneration experiments?

In amphibians, visible dedifferentiation of cells appears to be an indispensable preliminary to regeneration. The dedifferentiated cells are strictly local in origin. In other animals—for example, planarians, coelenterates, and annelids—there is evidence of the immigration of cells from parts of the body not immediately associated with the regeneration. In the majority of cases, these migratory cells appear to be nondifferentiated embryonic cells rather than dedifferentiated cells. In turbellarians, annelids, and tunicates, they will produce all tissues of the regenerate except the epidermis, nervous system, and gut. They are pluripotent rather than totipotent.

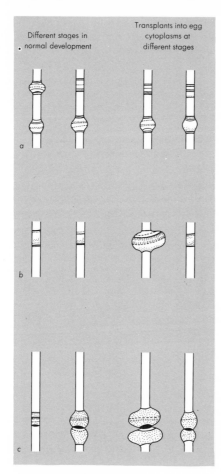

Fig. 12.3. The changes that occur in the appearance of the salivary chromosomes (a, b, and c) when they are exposed to cytoplasms from normally developing eggs of Drosophila. The swollen regions are sites of active synthesis. These sites vary at different times during development, and their activity may be enhanced or suppressed by changing the cytoplasmic environment of the chromosomes. Based on Heinrich Kroeger, "The Induction of New Puffing Patterns by Transplantation of Salivary Gland Nuclei into Egg Cytoplasma of Drosophila," *Chromosoma*, 11 (1960).

Regeneration, therefore, involves the dedifferentiation of cells with a subsequent redifferentiation along a different pathway, or the migration of a special pluripotent and relatively undifferentiated type of cell. The former method is the more important in higher forms, the latter in lower animals. The ability to dedifferentiate, coupled with the power to redifferentiate, sometimes to a different type of tissue, argues against irreversible changes during differentiation. On the other hand, the necessity for laying aside an undifferentiated type of cell for regeneration argues for the inability of the differentiated cells to dedifferentiate.

Aging

Differentiation may break down, particularly during aging and senescence. In plants, the possibility of continuous vegetative propagation allows the aging process to be prolonged indefinitely. In fungi, such prolonged aging leads to a gradual loss of vigor and of the ability to differentiate the structures associated with sexual and asexual reproduction. In *Aspergillus glaucus*, the final consequence is the condition known as vegetative death; in *Podospora anserina*, it is the condition known as senescence. Both show strict extrachromosomal inheritance (see Chapter 6). Similar, but less well-understood, upsets are found in other plants.

In lower animals, the effects of prolonged aging can be followed in vegetatively maintained clones. In *Paramecium*, for example, the degenerative changes resulting from aging follow much the same course as in fungi. But the basis of the degeneration apparently differs. It has been traced to a progressive imbalance in the chromosomal complement of the macronucleus, rather than to changes in the extranuclear complement. Hence the loss of developmental potential following aging may result from degenerate changes in the extrachromosomal system or in differentiated somatic nuclei.

Germ lines

If differentiation involves persistent changes in either chromosomal or extrachromosomal material, then, as Kenneth Mather and I have argued, either these changes must be reversed during gametogenesis or such changes must not occur in the germ line. Otherwise, the zygote produced at fertilization will not possess the totipotency of its counterpart of the previous generation. The alternatives are, therefore, (1) the restoration of totipotency during gamete or zygote formation, and (2) the preservation of totipotency from one generation to the next in the germ line. These alternatives have their equivalents in the two methods of regeneration, namely, by dedifferentiation and by nondifferentiated cells.

In *Paramecium*, the first two divisions of the fusion nucleus separate the micronuclear and macronuclear material. The micronuclei and the germ line preserve their totipotency from one generation to another. The macronucleus, whose activity largely determines the somatic phenotype, differentiates irreversibly during development and aging. Hence in *Paramecium*, totipotency is preserved in the germ line, while that of the soma is lost during development. This situation appears to be general in animals. As early as the first cleavage division of the zygote, the presumptive germ line and soma are often separated. Differentiation, involving irreversible changes in the heritable complement, may then proceed in the soma without any loss of the totipotency of the germ line. Initially, the difference between the germ line and somatic cells is purely extrachromosomal, although the difference may be subsequently consolidated by chromosome diminution or nuclear differentiation in the soma.

In the fungi, the future germ line and soma are indistinguishable. Both arise continuously throughout the life of a colony from the same hyphal-growing tips. Hence any changes that occur before or during the differentiation of the sexual stage must be restored to their original state in the germ line. In some fungi, the cumulative loss in vigor and developmental capacity that result from repeated vegetative or asexual propagations are restored by sexual reproduction. Thus in the absence of a distinct germ line, totipotency of the zygote is apparently achieved by a process of restoration. Mather and Jinks have proposed two mechanisms for this restoration. The first assumes that there is an active restoration of the extrachromosomal material during sexual reproduction. The second assumes that only cell lineages with totipotent extrachromosomal complements successfully complete the complex differentiation leading to sexual spore production. In this case the restoration of totipotency is the result of selection within the clone.

No observations have been made that can discriminate between these alternative explanations. Nevertheless, it is worth pursuing the arguments for and against them. There is, for example, no doubt that chromosomal genes often show unique and intense activities during gametogenesis. Hence any developmental potential that depends ultimately on gene products produced solely during this period will be restored only by sexual reproduction. On the other hand, there is some evidence that totipotency is restored by selection in the case of certain mutants of *Aspergillus nidulans*. For example, J. H. Croft has shown that the minute variant segregates persistently among vegetative hyphae, asexual spores, and hülle cells but never appears in its own sexual progeny, which is invariably wild type. If, however, vegetative hyphae and asexual spores are taken from the vicinity of the sexual fruiting bodies, the perithecia, they too are almost exclusively wild type. Similarly, the hyphae and asexual spores of the red variant produced in the vicinity of its sterile fruiting bodies, are also predominantly wild type. Thus the hyphae and asexual spores produced in those parts of the clones where the fruiting bodies subsequently develop have a more wild-type extrachromosomal complement than the rest of the colony. The wild-type extrachromosomal complement of the sexual spores is, therefore, a characteristic of the cell lineages that have the capacity to produce the sexual stage, and not an end product of sexual reproduction itself. Hence selection can contribute to the superiority of the sexual progeny of a degenerate colony, and to the ability of sexual reproduction to restore totipotency.

Conclusions

The totipotency of a zygote resides partly in its extrachromosomal material. This material includes the products of chromosomal gene activity as well as components whose structure and function are partly under plasmagene control. The segregation of the extrachromosomal material during the cleavage of a zygote is an essential first step in the differentiation of multicellular animals. Nuclear changes also occur, but they are secondary. They are consequences rather than causes of differentiation, although they later become the cause of further differentiation.

Because persistent changes in the heritable material occur during differentiation, special provisions must be made to preserve or restore the totipotency of the germ line and the pluripotency of the cells responsible for regeneration.

References

Briggs, Robert W., and T. J. King, "Nucleo-cytoplasmic Interactions in Eggs and Embryos," in *The Cell,* Jean Brachet and A. E. Mirsky, eds. (New York: Academic Press, Inc., 1959), I, 537.

Geyer-Duszynska, I., "Experimental Research on Chromosome Elimination in Cecidomyiidae (Diptera)," *J. Exp. Zool., 141* (1959), 391.

Gurdon, J. B., "Nuclear Transplantation in Amphibia and the Importance of Stable Nuclear Change in Promoting Cellular Differentiation," *Quart. Rev. Biol., 38* (1963), 54.

Mather, Kenneth, "Nucleus and Cytoplasm in Differentiation," *Symp. Soc. Exp. Biol., 2* (1948), 196.

———, and John L. Jinks, "Cytoplasm in Sexual Reproduction," *Nature, 182* (1958), 1188.

Questions

12.1. What is the contribution of extrachromosomal hereditary material to (a) the gradients within the eggs of multicellular animals, and (b) the determination of the plane and position of cleavage? What are the respective roles of (a) and (b) in differentiation?

12.2. The nuclei of fully determined cells of an amphibian embryo are frequently totipotent when transferred to the extranuclear material of an egg. What light does this observation throw on the mechanism of differentiation?

12.3. Why are the problems of differentiation, regeneration, and the separation of a germ line interrelated?

Thirteen

Extrachromosomal Variation
and Evolution

Variation in natural populations

Most, if not all, plasmagene mutations studied in
the laboratory result in a defective or even a lethal phenotype. Hence, they are unlikely to constitute an important
component of the variation encountered in natural populations. In this respect, they are like major gene mutations. And just as gene mutations may persist for some
time in the heterozygous state, providing that they are
recessive, a plasmagene mutation may similarly survive
in the heteroplasmic state. But this only delays the ultimate loss of the mutant. Sorting out of the heteroplasmon
will continually expose the mutant homoplasmon to the
action of natural selection.

A number of factors can further delay the loss of the
mutant, or stop it completely. The first of these is an
advantage of the heteroplasmon over its component homoplasmons. Such an advantage has been observed where
both component homoplasmons were mutants, but this
advantage did not lead to the persistence of the heteroplasmic state (see Chapter 8). Nevertheless, this example
raises the possibility that the equivalent of the permanent heterozygote might exist at the extrachromosomal
level. An advantage in rate of growth is shown by the
stable heteroplasmic red variant of *Aspergillus nidulans*
over its wild-type component and, of course, over its
mutant component, which is presumed lethal. This ad-

162

vantage, however, is confined to rate of growth, since the heteroplasmon is both sexually sterile and a poor sporulator. But in the
fungi, the long-term advantages of sexual reproduction are often
discounted by the short-term advantages of vegetative vigor, as, for
example in the imperfect fungi; hence vegetative vigor may be sufficient to ensure the short-term survival of a heteroplasmon in nature.

The prospective flexibility of the heteroplasmic state is potentially
as great as the proven flexibility of the heterokaryotic state in fungi.
By changes in the relative frequencies of the different forms of a
determinant, a heteroplasmon may exist in a number of alternative
phenotypes. Such a range of alternative phenotypes has been obtained
for some heteroplasmons. However, these alternatives have not as yet
been produced automatically in response to different environmental
conditions, and there is no evidence that any change so induced would
be adaptive. On the other hand, heteroplasmons have been found in
wild populations of *Penicillium* species as frequently as heterokaryons.
Furthermore, one of the commonest types of variation in *Fungi imper-
fecti*, known as the "dual phenomenon," is sometimes heteroplasmic
in origin. It is possible, therefore, that the prospective advantages of
heteroplasmons may indeed be exploited, at least among nonsexual
fungi.

The suppressiveness of many extrachromosomal mutants in the
heteroplasmic state, while on the one hand exposing them to the action
of natural selection, on the other hand leads to their persistence. For
example, suppressiveness is an important contributor to the persistence
of the mutant component of the red variant, and the ability of mutants
to suppress their wild-type homologue in any cell they enter is responsible for the invasive spread of a number of mutants to neighboring
cells of the same or a different organism. Clearly, the ability to multiply at the expense of its normal homologue and to spread by cell
contact could place a suppressive mutant at an immediate, but not
necessarily permanent, advantage. By replacing its normal homologue
in all cells to which it can gain access, a suppressive mutant is at the
same time destroying its sole means of survival. Hence any success
it might enjoy is limited in both time and space.

Not all suppressive mutants have a disastrous effect on the phenotypes of the cells they enter. Those mutants that produce only slight
defects might, therefore, achieve a balance between the selective disadvantage of the cells that contain them in competition with the wild-
type homoplasmon and the advantage in replication of the mutant
homologue over the wild-type homologue when in competition within
the same cell. The latter advantage, however, is not unconditional. A
suppressive mutant may itself be suppressed in association with a
different genome. Thus the genomes of different wild isolates of *Aspergillus nidulans* have differential effects on the relative rates of replication of the mutant and wild-type homologues of the heteroplasmic red
variant. There seems little doubt, therefore, that gene modifiers of the

rate of replication of suppressive plasmagenes are present in wild populations.

Most extrachromosomal mutants are obviously defective or lethal under normal circumstances, and can often survive only in a heteroplasmic state. Those arising specifically in response to a change in the environment, however, might be expected to have some adaptive significance, at least under the environmental conditions that induced them. Chapter 7 has already pointed out that this is not generally the case but there are exceptions, for example, the extrachromosomally inherited mutants of *Chlamydomonas*, which are resistant to 500 μ gm. of streptomycin (see Fig. 4.4). Ruth Sager has shown that these are induced by streptomycin and, of course, that the mutants are the only individuals to survive in its presence. It seems, therefore, a reasonable extrapolation to suggest that in nature, some of the extrachromosomal changes that occur in response to changes in the environment may be adaptive, at least while the conditions that induced them persist.

The advantage will be transitory unless the capacity for further change, or even a reversal of the initial change, is retained. If the initial change involved the loss of a plasmagene, it would be irreversible. If only a change or loss of function of a plasmagene were involved, it might be reversible by backmutation. Some categories of change, however, are capable of both further change and reversal of an initial change, for example, those changes that produce a heteroplasmic rather than a new homoplasmic state. The heteroplasmic state retains the capacity for reversal and further change as long as it persists.

Speciation

Just as it is useful to consider the possible significance of the kinds of extrachromosomal changes brought about in the laboratory for variation and adaptation in nature, it is also helpful to consider the significance of extrachromosomal differences occurring in nature. Plasmon differences between varieties and species are quite common in the Plant Kingdom. They have been found between varieties of *Epilobium hirsutum* collected from different geographical areas and between different species of the genera *Epilobium, Cirsium, Streptocarpus, Oenothera, Funaria, Physcomitrium,* and *Neurospora*.

The species *E. hirsutum* has become differentiated into a number of distinct plasmotypes, and the majority of plants in a particular geographical region belong to the same plasmotype. For example, in the vicinity of Jena and in Thuringia, 41 per cent of all plants tested have a similar plasmotype, namely, that referred to as Jena (see Chapter 11). Outside this region, Jena occurs only as a rarity, constituting less than 2 per cent of the plants tested. This association between a particular plasmotype and a particular geographical area suggests the evolution of types better suited to local environments. Indeed, this process appears to have resulted in varieties that border on becoming distinct species. For even those varieties that are still interfertile often produce abnormal F_1's on crossing. Furthermore, the later generations from the fertile crosses give varying proportions of abnormal individuals with similar or more extreme developmental upsets than the original F_1. It is perhaps not surprising, therefore, that Peter Michaelis finds that the species of the genus *Epilobium* often differ in their plasmotypes as well as in their genotypes.

The species of the genus *Streptocarpus* also differ in their plasmotypes. For example, Friedrich Oehlkers has shown that the plasmons of three different species of this genus inhibit the female fertility of *S. Wendlandii*, while the plasmon of the latter produces male sterility when associated with the genomes of these species. In the genus *Oenothera* speciation depends as much on plastogene differences as on genome differences (see Chapter 11).

So far, naturally occurring plasmon differences have been clearly demonstrated for only one species in the Animal Kingdom, the mosquito *Culex pipiens*. This species, like *E. hirsutum*, can be divided into a number of geographical races (Fig. 13.1), some of which are interfertile if the cross is made in one direction, while others will not cross in either direction. We cannot analyze the cause of the latter, but where the cross can still be made in one direction, analysis is possible. H. Laven has shown in an extensive crossing program that the unidirectional fertility is due to plasmon differences between the races. These plasmon differences are remarkably stable; they have been transmitted without change by the maternal parents through sixty successive backcrosses to males from different races. It seems, therefore, that the plasmon determines the ability to cross in this mosquito.

These examples show that the plasmon, by mutation and selection, can become adapted, or rather coadapted with the genome, to local environmental conditions. In some instances, this process has led to crossing barriers, isolation, and speciation.

Evolution

An old theory, which still finds wide support, claims that the fundamental differences between species, genera, and the higher taxonomic units are due to plasmon differences, and that only the differences within species, that is, the more trivial differences between varieties and strains, are due to gene differences. This theory initially gained experimental support in the 1920's and 1930's from investigators who, on crossing different species and different genera, found that the wider the taxonomic difference between two parents, the greater, in general, was the difference between their reciprocal hybrids. At this time, of course, almost all the examples of extrachromosomal heredity came from wide outcrosses. This situation has now changed. Far more examples are now based on differences within species, and many of them are due to spontaneous or induced mutations within clones. These differences are as great or greater than those found in crossing different species and genera.

On the other hand, it is now often suggested that plasmagenes are concerned primarily with the control of the more "fundamental"

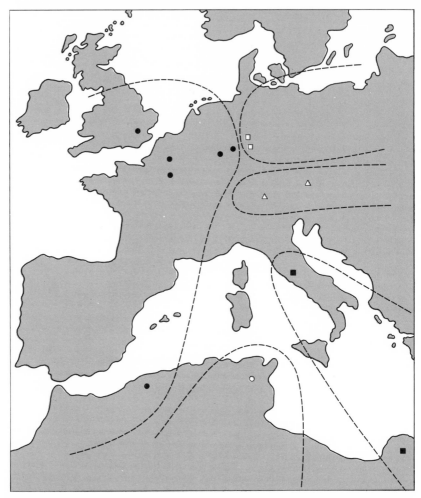

Fig. 13.1. The distribution of five European "crossing types" of the mosquito *Culex pipiens*. Some of these crossing types, for example, ○ and ●, will not cross at all, others, for example, ● and △, will cross in one direction but not in the other. Individuals belonging to the same "crossing type" will cross in both directions. Based on H. Laven, "Speciation by Cytoplasmic Isolation in the *Culex pipiens* Complex," *Cold Spring Harbor Symp. Quant. Biol.*, 24 (1959).

characteristics of the cell. It is true that plasmagene mutations affect such important functions as respiration and photosynthesis. Indeed, the bearers of the plasmagenes may well be the extrachromosomal cell constituents concerned with these processes (see Chapter 3). But as

Kenneth Mather has pointed out, these "fundamental" characteristics of the cell are equally subject to chromosomal gene control (see Chapter 10). He has also drawn attention to the difficulties that would arise from accepting this interpretation of the role of the plasmon. For example, we should have to recognize a process of macroevolution that differs from microevolution. Up to a certain point, or at a certain stage, evolutionary change would proceed by the accumulation of adaptations, which depend essentially on the mutual adjustment of chromosomal genes with one another and with the plasmagenes. Beyond this point, or stage, evolutionary change would have to spring from modifications that are confined to the plasmon and brought about by forces of which we know nothing.

Balanced out, therefore, the evidence suggests that the most important influence of the plasmon, from an evolutionary point of view, is its ability to produce more or less effective crossing barriers. It cannot, however, be held responsible for a special type of evolution that has to do with the emergence of the higher taxonomic units.

Concluding remarks

The final chapter of this study of extrachromosomal heredity has shown that the system whose properties have been elucidated by cytological observations and breeding experiments plays a role in nature. This role ranges from the release of variation to the erection of crossing barriers, and hence to the emergence of species and higher taxonomic units. But the extrachromosomal system does not act alone. At all levels its activities interact with those of the chromosomal system. It is the coadaptation of genome and plasmon to a particular environment rather than changes in the plasmon alone that has led to the divergence of races of *Epilobium, Oenothera, Streptocarpus,* and *Culex,* and ultimately to their speciation.

References

Cleland, R. E., "The Cytogenetics of *Oenothera,*" *Advan. Genet., 11* (1962), 147.

Jinks, John L., "Cytoplasmic Inheritance in Fungi," in *Methodology in Basic Genetics,* W. J. Burdette, ed. (San Francisco: Holden-Day, Inc., 1963).

Mather, Kenneth, "Genes and Cytoplasm in Development," *Handb. Pflanzenphysiologie, 15* (1958), 39.

Sager, Ruth, "Streptomycin as a Mutagen for Non-chromosomal Genes," *Proc. Nat. Acad. Sci. U.S., 48* (1962), 2018.

Questions

13.1. Two geographical races of a plant species are interfertile if crossed in one direction, but sterile if crossed in the other. Suggest reasons for this. How would you test their validity?

13.2. "The fundamental differences between species, genera, and higher taxonomic units are based on cytoplasmic differences, and only the trivial differences between varieties and strains are due to genes." Why did this theory initially gain support from the study of extrachromosomal heredity? Why is its validity now doubted?

Index

A

Acetabularia, 144

Acridine dyes: 18, 84-86, 123; acriflavine, 67; euflavine, 67; mutagenic effect, 67, 84-86

Adenosine triphosphate (ATP), 14, 144

Aging: of spores, 101; in *Aspergillus,* 68, 159; in *Paramecium,* 159; in *Podospora,* 68, 159

Algae, 10

Amoeba: 143; extranuclear determination in, 142; nuclear size, 141 (control of, 141); nuclear transplantation, 141

Amphibia: eggs of, 9 (centriole of, 39); gray crescent, 148

Aneuploidy: 48, 54, 55, 59, 75; in *Rana,* 142

Antigens (*see* Serotypes)

Anthoceros, chloroplast behavior in, 16

Antirrhinum: dauermodifications of, 82; maternal inheritance in, 39

Arbacia: development of, 148; effect of lithium on, 149; mitochondrial gradients in, 149

Arcella, dauermodifications of, 82

Arlett, C.F., 57, 76, 131, 132

Ascaris, chromosome diminution in, 150, 152

Ascidia, muscle differentiation in, 152

Ascospores: of *Aspergillus,* 50; of *Neurospora,* 42; of yeast, 49

Asexual spores: of *Aspergillus,* 94; of *Neurospora,* 28

Aspergillus: asexual spores of, 94; heterokaryon tests in, 60; heterokaryosis in, 74; homokaryons of, 69; persistent segregation in, 94, 109; restoration of totipotency in, 160; unstable mutants of, 57

Aspergillus glaucus: 53, 59; aging in, 68, 159; compact mutant of, 68; conidial mutant of, 54, 69, 98; gene differences in, 54; hyphal anastomosis in, 69; vegetative death in, 61, 68, 69, 74, 87, 98, 101

Aspergillus nidulans: 59; dikaryons of, 50; extrachromosomal mutants, 90; gene differences in, 50; heterokaryons of, 50; heterokaryon test in, 59; hyphal anastomosis in, 50, 69; life cycle, 50; minute mutant, 57, 67, 78, 160 (effects of gene mutants on, 133); mycelial mutant, 67; nonsexual mutants, 50, 60; perithecia of, 50; purple mutant, 54 (effects of gene mutants on, 133); red mutant, 57, 68, 74, 100, 160, 162, 163 (effects of gene mutants on, 133; persistence of, 163; stability of, 131, 132); sexual reproduction of, 50; somatic segregation in, 75

Aspidistra, chloroplast development in, 16

Asters, 6, 8, 11

Augmentor gene, of *Chlamydomonas,* 129

Autogamy, in *Paramecium:* 23; gene segregation at, 25; induction of, 25

Autotrophs, 17

Auxotrophic mutants, of *Chlamydomonas,* 68

Axial filaments, 8, 9

B

Backmutation: 88, 118, 164; of plastids, 88

Bacteriophage, 121

Balbiani rings: 157; modification of, 157; and RNA synthesis, 157

Barbulanympha: aberrant individuals of, 11; axostyles of, 11; centriole cycle of, 7, 11; flagella of, 11; parabasal bodies of, 11